GEOLOGY EXPLAINED IN DORSET

GEOLOGY EXPLAINED
IN DORSET

by
JOHN W. PERKINS, BA, FGS, FRGS

*Illustrations by
the Author*

DAVID & CHARLES
NEWTON ABBOT · LONDON
NORTH POMFRET (VT) · VANCOUVER

ISBN 0 7153 7319 6
Library of Congress Catalog Card Number 76–54070

© John W. Perkins 1977

Set in 11 on 13 Plantin
and printed in Great Britain by
Redwood Burn Limited, Trowbridge & Esher
for David & Charles (Publishers) Limited
Brunel House   Newton Abbot   Devon

Published in the United States of America
by David & Charles Inc
North Pomfret   Vermont 05053   USA

Published in Canada
by Douglas David & Charles Limited
1875 Welch Street   North Vancouver   BC

Contents

Introduction

Containing mainly Jurassic, Cretaceous and Tertiary beds, Dorset is one of the premier training grounds of British geology, a must for all who love the subject whether their interest is amateur or professional.

> 'Such a variety of scenery, of floras and faunas, and, in the realm of geology, of formations, fossils, structures and erosion features'
> 'the best tectonic features in the Mesozoic and Tertiary areas of England'
> 'on its geological variety ... depend all the other qualities of this favoured region'
>
> —W. J. Arkell

Good exposures and fossil faunas have ensured that the local names of Kimmeridge and Portland are used the world over as stratigraphical stage names in the geology of the Jurassic. The Oxford Clay and Corallian beds also have their best exposure and development in England here.

The area of study is the southern part of the re-defined county, one of the few to expand in the 1974 re-organisation of local government. Bournemouth, Boscombe and Christchurch were added to the county, forming a major extension to the area of its Tertiary strata. A rough northern boundary is taken along the A35 and space alone prevents the treatment of the rest of inland Dorset.

Always remember to keep to the coastal, country and geological codes. *Never* enter the army gunnery or tank ranges (see page 130). Do not damage exposures or take more than one example of any fossil or mineral specimen. Carefully label and store any that you do collect for study. Do not collect from Nature Reserves or Sites of Special Scientific Interest. Description of any site here is not a passport to access nor does it mean that permission will be given. These rules are simple—and the means whereby many more generations of geology enthusiasts will be able to continue the study and enjoyment of South Dorset.

Dorset geology is the geology of profusion—and profusion can soon become confusion if the student has no orderly plan of study. Chapter 1 outlines the historical geology of the area. Then the following Chapters 2–8 take the reader up through coastal exposures mainly, illustrating the rocks in their order of formation. When this sequence has been studied it then forms a basis for understanding the more complex coastal areas. The inland geology is dealt with in similar fashion—areas in order of formation first, more complex areas last. The final chapters deal with modern coastal features and the stone trades.

The whole of Dorset is covered by Geological Survey maps in print and there are also two postwar memoirs. Use of these and the Ordnance Survey maps is essential. Grid references are given in the text and for all figures. The profusion of fossils found in Dorset and the small number which can be illustrated here make the British Museum (Natural History) handbooks *Mesozoic Fossils* and *Caenozoic Fossils* essential companions, while the (Penguin) *Dictionary of Geology* will be found to be a useful reference book.

CHAPTER 1

Geology and Dorset

The geology of Dorset is more than just the story of its Jurassic, Cretaceous and Tertiary rocks. Imprinted on these are the records of still older events in the earth's history. Obviously there is a basement of older rocks beneath Dorset and the story of the county may be conveniently taken up in the Palaeozoic era, about 350 million years ago.

FAR AWAY AND LONG AGO

In those unimaginably far off days the world was very different. For convenience, modern place names must be used to describe it. England was about 16° south of the Equator, enjoying a tropical Caribbean type of climate and close to the northern margin of an ocean which later became deltaic and swampy, accumulating the Carboniferous limestones, shales and coal measures. About 290 million years ago the ocean began to close as neighbouring continents drifted together folding its sediments and creating new lands from them—the Hercynian mountain building period. Creating much of South-West England, among other areas, the event also saw the intrusion of the granite batholith nowadays exposed amid those Palaeozoic rocks as the string of moorlands running down through Devon and Cornwall.

The movements welded the continents of the world into a super continent called Pangea which then drifted slowly northwards, taking the rock and fossil record of its earlier history across the Equator. England was part of its semi-arid heart. There erosion of the folded Palaeozoic rocks commenced at once and, spanning over into the Mesozoic era, produced the New Red Sandstones of the Permo-Triassic periods. Pangea travelled from 10°N to 30°N at this time. Red sandstones produced in its semi-arid heartland can be seen just west of Dorset along the Devon coast and traced towards the Palaeozoic rocks from which they were eroded, eg near Torquay (*Geology Explained in South and East Devon,* David & Charles, 1971). No doubt Permo-Triassic rocks also exist beneath Dorset, where some have suggested that they may contain salt deposits as in other parts of England, and have influenced folds produced in the succeeding Jurassic and Cretaceous deposits at later periods.

195 million years ago, having reached 30–35°N, the great continent Pangea was moving out of the tropical climates and also beginning to break up—the Americas began to drift away westward and the Central Atlantic was formed. The sea flooded parts of the arid heartland for the first time in about 100 million years, depositing the Rhaetic beds seen locally just west of the Dorset boundary at Culverhole Point. The developing Atlantic Ocean then became a major influence on Jurassic and Cretaceous geology. During these periods the northward drift took England from 35° to 45° N.

THE JURASSIC DEPOSITS

The story of the Jurassic period is one of subsidence into fully marine conditions. Swamps, deltas and land areas were unknown in Dorset from Liassic up to Portlandian times. Over England as a whole the subsidence was uneven and several basins of deposition were formed—the South West, the Midlands, Yorkshire—with the intervening ridges often along the lines of old Palaeozoic-bedded folds, eg the Mendips. North America was now separating from North Africa. The gradual opening of the Atlantic affected the old fold axes from time to time, and gently stirred others beneath the basins of deposition. This upset the sequences of rock forming within the basins and frequently changed their geography, sometimes enclosing at others uniting them by connecting channels. Some Jurassic beds contain the record of these minor adjustments in planes of erosion, non-sequences, and minor unconformities.

The Lower Jurassic (Lias) of Dorset is clayey in character. It was deposited in rather enclosed basins where restricted water movement created poor bottom environments with precipitation of iron sulphide (pyrites). Finely divided in the sediments, this gives them their dark grey colour. The greatest puzzle associated with these beds is the origin of their limy banding, particularly developed in the Blue Lias at their base (Chapter 2).

The first of the disturbances in the sequence created the remarkable Junction Bed between the Middle and Upper Lias (page 40). It represents a prolonged period of shallow water conditions with several small intervals of uplift and erosion. Afterwards the character of Lias deposition changed with sandy deltaic conditions spreading south. The Bridport and Yeovil Sands resulted and were followed by a second period of disturbance during the deposition of the Inferior Oolite. This time the cause was an even older line of structural weakness which runs under Dorset in a north-south direction. Known as the Bath Axis, it extends from the Malvern Hills south under Bath, Radstock, Yeovil and Bridport. It greatly affected the thicknesses of the Lower and Middle Inferior Oolite. Its activity had ceased by upper Inferior Oolite times, however, a feature especially important in the deposition of the Sherborne building stone in North Dorset.

So, up to the beginning of Middle Jurassic times, deposition in Dorset was disturbed twice by reactivation of old folds in the basement, including the north-south Bath Axis and east-west Hercynian folds representing buried extensions of the Palaeozoic rocks of South-West England. The latter meet the Bath Axis at right angles, probably under the Weymouth anticline (Chapter 4) and the Marshwood pericline (Chapter 11).

Marine conditions continued through upper Jurassic times, up to the formation of the Portland Stone near the top of the succession. The seas, constantly changing and subsiding but never very deep, created the great variety of clays, sandstones, grits and limestones from the Fullers Earth up to the Portland Stone. The variety of material provides fine opportunities to study how fossil faunas change with varying environments.

In Oxford Clay times muddy sediments formed in rather restricted waters. Drifted plant debris from neighbouring land areas was buried in the sediment. Iron pyrites was precipitated again, giving the rocks colours reminiscent of the earlier Lias beds. As a result fossils buried in the Oxford Clay are often found as decalcified impressions—for ground-water moving through the beds since has combined with the sulphide of the iron pyrites to make weak sulphuric acid and dissolve the fossil shells. On the other hand it has then combined with the calcium of the shells to form calcium sulphate—gypsum—so although they are poor in fossil preservation the clays do contain fine selenite (crystalline gypsum).

The Corallian beds which follow indicate clearer water, but there were two short relapses back to current-less muddy conditions when only large oysters were able to survive on the sea bed (Chapter 4). Whenever the currents increased, sands were washed in, but when sediment supply dropped, and the waters remained clear and well aerated, limestones were formed. Thus the Corallian deposits reveal a detailed and changing record, an interval between the great muddy phases of the Oxford and Kimmeridge Clays. The latter again represents restricted water deposition, with pyrites formation—most famous in modern times for its spontaneous combustion in the burning cliffs.

Towards the end of the Jurassic the warm watered seas were filled with Portland Sands and became shallow, clear and aerated, ie conditions similar to the modern Bahamas banks and the great Portland Stone limestone deposition occurred. In the final episode of Jurassic times these deposits were upheaved to create an area of lakes and brackish swamps, a halfway world between marine and land conditions which provided a great mixture of environments and fossil life—the Purbeck Beds.

The date was about 140 million years ago. Still opening up by means of its spreading sea floor ridge, the Atlantic was extending north into the Bay of Biscay, with Spain rotating anticlockwise to open up the bay area. Perhaps it was then that Britain really became a part of the European continent, for had the spreading continued to develop north-eastwards we could have been on the far side of the ridge and gone west with North America! However, the Biscay spreading ceased in the Lower Cretaceous and a change of direction occurred, the widening ocean extending north-west towards the Labrador Sea.

THE CRETACEOUS AND TERTIARY DEPOSITS

As the Cretaceous period opened, the Purbeck intertidal and swampy lands were submerged allowing a great delta of one or more rivers to build the sandy Wealden Beds across the area. Much of this material appears to have been washed east from South-West England.

Like the Jurassic, the Cretaceous period was twice interrupted by earth movements but of a stronger character. The first upheaval followed the formation of the Wealden Beds, creating the great Abbotsbury Fault (Chapter 15), and in other places throwing the Jurassic into folds which were quickly eroded, exposing beds as far down as the Oxford Clay and Forest Marble in places. Marine conditions followed the disturbance in a submergence known as the Aptian transgression which led to the deposition of the Lower Greensand (Chapter 7).

The Lower Greensand is not well exposed in Dorset but it is of great interest since it occurs only in the eastern part of the county. To the west (page 94), it was overlapped by the Gault and Upper Greensand which, aided by a second tilting and submergence of the region, were able to extend much farther west, forming a second unconformable sheet of deposits extending into Devon. These rocks are a major landscape feature of West Dorset (Chapters 2 and 3), the great Cretaceous unconformity. This second transgression which created it is named the Albian transgression. Memorise the two—Aptian followed by Lower Greensand, Albian followed by Gault, Upper Greensand and Chalk.

In the Upper Cretaceous, deposition was dominated by chalk, nearly pure calcium carbonate which covered vast tracts of Europe and probably formed off desert coasts. Continued northerly drift was taking Europe up to latitude $45°N$. This was 82–60 million years ago. The Labrador Sea and the North Atlantic Ocean were opening up, but 65 million years ago, as the Cretaceous period drew to a close, another change occurred. Spreading which had then reached $53°N$ was reduced in the Labrador Sea and a new break developed between Greenland and the Rockall Plateau northwest of Scotland, the final separation of Europe and North America.

In Britain and NW Europe the associated event was an irregular upheaval, creating land areas and shallow basins in which a semi-tropical life flourished. It must seem that the geology of Dorset is dominated by numbers: two notable earth disturbances in the Jurassic and two in the Cretaceous, two great clay depositions—the Oxford and Kimmeridge Clays. Now, in the early Tertiary era, another 'second' occurred. As in the Wealden, vast amounts of SW England type debris were again washed eastward by rivers, creating the Eocene sands, gravels and ball clays (Chapter 8 and 14). Of the rest of the Tertiary there is little rock record. The last great episode in the geological history of Dorset was the second (!) major folding of the rocks—the outer ripples of the great upheaval which created the mountains of southern Europe. Europe was then moving more slowly north than Africa which 'shunted' into it. Across southern England old basement folds were reactivated

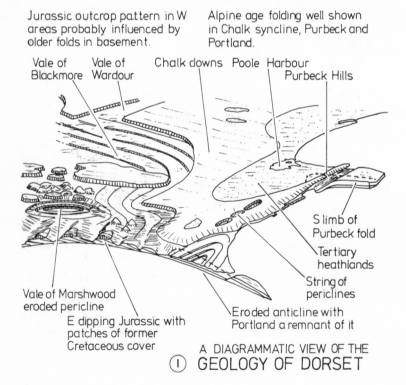

Jurassic outcrop pattern in W areas probably influenced by older folds in basement.

Alpine age folding well shown in Chalk syncline, Purbeck and Portland.

Vale of Blackmore   Vale of Wardour   Chalk downs   Poole Harbour   Purbeck Hills

S limb of Purbeck fold

Tertiary heathlands

String of periclines

Vale of Marshwood eroded pericline

E dipping Jurassic with patches of former Cretaceous cover

Eroded anticline with Portland a remnant of it

A DIAGRAMMATIC VIEW OF THE
① GEOLOGY OF DORSET

and, with their Jurassic and the Cretaceous covering, folded to form the Purbeck anticline (Chapter 12), folds of the Isle of Wight, the Weald, etc.

Little deposition has occurred in Dorset since. Coastal changes are the main features and these are described in Chapter 16. On the land areas the main activity has been erosional—re-working of the surface of rivers and by the cold conditions of the Ice Age, forming gravel terraces in areas like the heathlands (Chapter 14).

THE FOSSIL RECORD

Dorset rocks contain an enormous variety of fossils. Concerning the ammonites, remember that these began to evolve back in Carboniferous times from the goniatites. During the ensuing Permo-Triassic period, when Britain was in the semi-arid heart of Pangea, the ammonities were still evolving elsewhere. The result was that when marine conditions returned to Britain with the Jurassic vast numbers of new forms were ready to migrate into the area and spread widely over it. Their successive migrations and rapid evolution make them excellent zone fossils for Jurassic stratigraphy, but since their evolution occurred elsewhere their 'family tree' cannot be traced up through the British deposits. Only the pearly *Nautilus* survives now as a reminder of their innumerable species.

Fossils are important evidence of the environment responsible for the various beds, eg ammonites indicate marine conditions. So their absence from beds may be an equally valuable indicator. There are several ammonite 'gaps' in Dorset, eg Corallian, Purbeck and Wealden.

Corals are also important indicators, revealing warm clear well-lit waters. As with modern reefs, some other forms of life liked to be near them but others did not. For example, larger brittle lamellibranchs, *Trigonia, Lima, Pinna,* and ammonities all kept away, no doubt because their shells would have been smashed on the reefs. The Jurassic coral-bearing beds in Dorset are not very well endowed. Unfortunately the seas were never clear long enough. Only the swiftly migrating forms managed to reach the area in these brief intervals.

A third category of remains deserving special mention are the giant reptilian fossils—the Mesozoic was the era of reptiles and, like the ammonites, they became extinct at the end of it. Some of the great reptiles are possibly continued in the birds. Dorset is the premier English county for the study of reptilian remains— dinosaurs, ichthyosaurs, plesiosaurs, etc. In similar fashion to the ammonites, the reptiles had also evolved in the Permo-Triassic and came 'ready made' to the local Jurassic world. Again it is useful to remember the geography of the times—no English Channel and, in the early Mesozoic, no North Atlantic Ocean, so they were able to migrate from Europe to the USA.

A very readable account of the impact of the geological formations on the landscapes and soils of Dorset can be found in Wightman (see Bibliography).

CHAPTER 2

Jurassic of West Dorset Coast—1: Lyme Regis to Charmouth

Lyme Regis has probably had more geological publicity than most resorts. The town stands in the midst of a district renowned for landslips which, in their livelier moments, struck 'terror' into the less informed visitors of the last century. These people found the spontaneous combustion of iron pyrites in the local cliffs described in their papers as the 'Lyme volcano'. Later, nerves recovered, they went by the boatload to visit the slips west of the town. Periodically movements still occur, of course, and will continue to do so simply because of the nature of the rocks.

THE LIAS SUCCESSION

Belonging to the Lower Jurassic, the battleship-grey coloured rocks of this coast are known as the Lias, and the local base of the system lies only 6.4 km south-west of Lyme Regis at Culverhole Point in Devon. The Lias beds, the first fully marine deposits formed as the arid heart of Pangea broke up (Chapter 1), are fine-grained sediments, brought to the seas by the mature rivers of neighbouring land areas.

(Upper Lias Above)

Middle Lias (Chapter 3)
- Junction Bed (Middle & Upper Lias).
- Thorncombe and Downcliff Sands—grey, rather friable.
- Eype Clay with Starfish Bed at top—sticky clays with nodules.
- The Three Tiers—three stone bands.
- Green Ammonite Beds—named from the green calcite filling some ammonite chambers within them.

Lower Lias { Belemnite Marls—light grey with more stony beds than
              in the two groups beneath.
            Black Ven Marls—very dark grey colour.
            Shales with Beef—contain fibrous calcite, ie beef.
            Blue Lias—regular ribbed alternations of limestones and
              shales.

Above the Lias lies a great unconformity, capping the grey beds with younger, golden-weathering Upper Greensands from the Cretaceous period. These add the cliff-top splashes of colour at Black Ven, Stonebarrow and Golden Cap (Figure 3). In the author's *Geology Explained in South and East Devon* (David & Charles, 1971) chapters 9 and 10 and especially Figure 60 describe the relationship of this unconformable capping to the various beds beneath it.

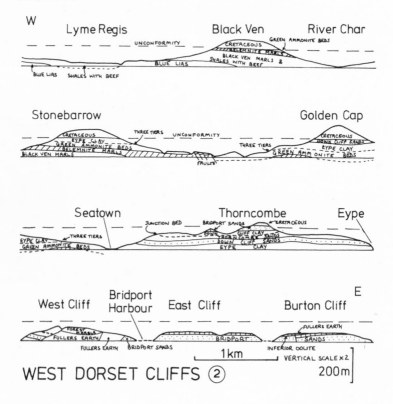

WEST DORSET CLIFFS ②

CHURCH CLIFFS

Lyme Regis stands on a small syncline, mainly of unstable Black Ven Marls. Take the path from Bridge Street to the east shore where the syncline rises to be replaced by a small anticline in Church Cliffs. The anticlinal axis runs out of the cliff towards the viewpoint, forming Broad Ledge on the shore below. Low tide is necessary to explore the shore towards Charmouth. Vertical sections of the Lias given on pages 12, 15, 19 and 21 of the Geological Survey Memoir *Geology of the Country Around Bridport and Yeovil,* 1958, are very useful.

Unfortunately the first part of the cliff is hidden behind a sea wall. In the nineteenth century, quarrymen worked the local limestone beds to meet the demand for stucco work removing 20,000 tonnes of limestone per year for burning. The trade continued into the early 1900s and as a result large cliff falls occurred. Church Cliffs had already suffered large slips in 1844, 1849 and 1867. Early protection work had limited success, but in

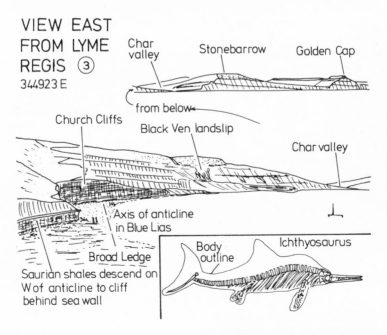

VIEW EAST FROM LYME REGIS ③
344923 E

Char valley   Stonebarrow   Golden Cap

from below

Church Cliffs   Black Ven landslip   Char valley

Axis of anticline in Blue Lias

Broad Ledge
Saurian shales descend on W of anticline to cliff behind sea wall

Body outline   Ichthyosaurus

1910 the sea wall had to be commenced. Only the central part of the anticline remains as a natural cliff, today crowned by the town rubbish dump, often burning in convincing imitation of the Lyme 'volcano' which ignited at the same spot!

Through the nineteenth century economic interest, the Blue Lias beds all have quarry names. The axis of Broad Ledge is Third Quick, with Gumption on either side. Other names were Specketty, Iron Ledge, Lower Skulls, Mongrel and Copper. The first limestone bed visible in the cliffs which does not close with the shore reefs is usually Third Quick, while the topmost one seen is Grey Ledge. The cliff then recedes in the Fish and Saurian Shales, among which a light grey band marks the position of Table Ledge, the Blue Lias and Shales with Beef junction.

We can now appreciate the reasons for the sea wall rather better. It is located where the weaker Fish and Saurian Shales come down to shore level on the west side of the anticline. Combined with quarrying these shales allowed the rapid erosion which occurred across Broad Ledge towards the town. Unfortunately, the sea wall now hides the area where the famous fossil collector of the last century, Mary Anning, found plesiosaur and ichthyosaur skeletons.

LYME, GEOLOGY AND MARY ANNING

Mary Anning was born in 1799, the daughter of Richard Anning, a Lyme Regis carpenter. His house was in Bridge Street and, like many local people then and since, he collected fossils from the local cliffs and sold them to visitors. This trade had first developed at Charmouth which was on the direct coach road between Exeter and Dorchester. Lyme Regis had improved connections with the road after 1758, but real opportunities for fossil dealing had to await the town's development as a watering place in the early nineteenth century. Richard Anning had as sound a knowledge as anyone in his day of the local specimens and geological conditions. He described the erosion of Church Cliffs. Within his memory, there had been gardens between the churchyard and the sea. No protection work was carried out on the cliff for about another twenty-five years—sometime after 1827—when the town's position as a watering place was established,

Mary Anning always maintained that her father had taught her all she knew about fossils, although he died when she was ten or eleven years old. If so he certainly instilled in her a skill in extracting and preparing them which was to prove useful to the early geologists with whom she collaborated. Lyme Regis was the nursery of leading geologists at this period. Henry de la Beche came to live there as a young boy. He knew Mary Anning all her life and they often went collecting together. De la Beche became the first director of the Geological Survey. William Buckland, who became the first professor of geology at Oxford in 1819, was also Mary Anning's companion on collecting excursions. Coneybeare was another friend—he was appointed vicar of Axminster in 1836. What a chance that all this geological talent was on hand at Christmas 1839 when the great landslips west of the town occurred! (*Geology Explained in South and East Devon*, pages 153–6).

Mary Anning's success with spectacular specimens began early. In 1811 when she was twelve years old she found an *Ichthyosaurus*. It took ten years to extract the 9m specimen, which was eventually sold for £23. It is not the one in the Natural History Museum, South Kensington, however—that was found in 1832. Other notable finds had been a complete *Plesiosaurus* in 1824 and another in 1828, plus the first British specimen of a flying reptile, the *Pterodactyl*. Ichthyosaurs were fish lizards resembling dolphins and could reach 5m in length and 1.5m in height.

In 1825 she moved to Broad Street, continuing her fossil collecting and supplying quantities of ammonites and belemnites to leading geologists. She knew Murchison, another geological pioneer, and experts in fossil ichthyology, Sir Philip Egerton and Lord Enniskillen. Mary Anning died at the young age of forty-seven and was buried in Lyme churchyard. There is a window in her memory in the church, partly subscribed by the Fellows of the Geological Society of London who, although she was not a member, accorded her the unusual distinction of an obituary address. 'The handmaid of geological science', she was a kind, practical and humble woman who developed with great skill the fossil material which she found. Her willing assistance made Lyme a cradle of British geology.

While in Lyme Regis, visit the Philpot Museum. It houses an interesting collection of fossils, with specimens from the Lias of North Yorkshire for comparison, a large *Ichthyosaurus*, and a picture of the original Anning fossil shop in Bridge Street, demolished in 1913. There is also a fossil shop opposite the museum.

THE BLUE LIAS PUZZLE

The regular alternation of limestones and shales in Church Cliffs is striking—and an outstanding geological problem! Formed originally as muds in the early Jurassic seas, the shales suggest deeper water phases, while the limestones should indicate periods of shallower, clearer water. The chief difference between the shales and limestones is in the amount of land-derived sediment they contain. The problem for the geologist is to decide whether this difference is primary or secondary—ie, was there a pulsating sea-floor, regularly varying in depth so that the sediments were deposited with the distinct layering we now see in them? Or was the original sediment uniform in character, a lime-rich mud deposit which was rhythmically unmixed on compaction, ie in a secondary process which occurred after formation and during the solidification of the deposit.

Examine the two types of bed closely. The limestones, light blue-grey in colour, are usually sharply defined beds although their surfaces vary from flat to very nodular. The flat-surfaced beds are often finely laminated but contain few fossils, whereas the latter have a variety of ammonites, gastropods, fragments of lignite and much pyrite material. Sometimes the limestones thicken around the larger fossil specimens, while in places in the Lias they pass into discontinuous layers of nodules, which are again closely related to larger fossil specimens. Composed of fine calcite crystals, the limestones reach 75–95 per cent calcium carbonate in composition.

The shales really include blue-grey marls and bituminous shales. The marls are similar to the limestones except that their calcium carbonate content is only 20–55 per cent. The bituminous shales have even less, under 10 per cent, and are dark blue-grey to black in colour.

It is the fossils of the Blue Lias which provide a guide to the early history of these beds. In the shales they are often crushed and decalcified, but in the limestones delicate details of their structure are perfectly preserved. As the calcium carbonate drew together into the limestone bands it preserved the fossils it enclosed, leaving others in the shales in a decalcified state. Some fossil evidence fits the opposite theory, however. This is the presence of myriad burrows of the trace fossil *Chondrites*. Although the precise creature which allowed the light and dark blue-grey sediments to mix by filling in its burrows has not been identified, in places the beds are riddled with evidence of its activity and the burrow form has been accurately reconstructed. Each Chondrites complex originated as a branching pattern from a central aperture on the sea bed. The importance of *Chondrites* is that it shows the sea bed was an inhabited place, that the layers of limestone and shale were once a part of it, ie primary deposits, different in character at the time of deposition.

The evidence can be summarised:

Favouring Primary Origin	*Favouring Secondary Origin*
1 Areal extent and uniform thickness of individual limestone beds	1 Better preservation of fauna in limestones and decalcified fauna in shales
2 Burrowing activity of trace fossils, eg *Chondrites*	2 The thicker the Blue Lias, the more limestone bands there are
3 Smaller size fauna in the bituminous shales supporting the idea of periods of stagnant anaerobic bottom water	3 Bands of ellipsoidal nodules
	4 Thickening of beds around large fossils

Geologists resolve the apparent conflict of evidence by accepting that both primary and secondary factors have contributed to the rhythmic succession. What was it that caused the primary variation? Looking at it from the viewpoint of the differing proportions of land-derived mud present in the shales and limestones, rainfall or tectonic action could have been responsible. From the calcium-carbonate point of view, however, the rivers supplying mud to the Lias seas were draining neighbouring unsubmerged remnants of the old Permo-Triassic landscape. In parts of that landscape older Carboniferous limestones were still standing as hill remnants, in areas like the Mendips. In arid landscapes generally, accumulations of limestone also occur just below the surface, representing incipient soils known as calcretes. The advent of a river regime in these areas must have produced a high discharge of calcium carbonate into the early Jurassic seas. However, the importance of this factor has still to be decided. There is certainly a high proportion of strontium present in the Blue Lias which may well have been washed in from the Permo-Triassic landscape. As celestite, strontium sulphate occurs as nodules in Triassic marls, eg near Yate, Gloucestershire. In the Blue Lias the strontium is more concentrated in the shale beds, suggesting that these do represent times of greater mud influx.

Another line of research has been into the precipitation of calcium carbonate by bacteria in seawater—this increases with high temperatures in well-lit waters. The sea-floor was stagnant and poisonously sulphurous, stunting the fauna which accumulated on its anaerobic floor sometimes. This formed the bituminous shales, some of them receiving large quantities of land mud and becoming marly in character. But at other times improvements in the circulation and slight elevation allowed more calcium-carbonate rich beds to form. Geologists conclude that original variation in the Blue Lias was due to varying depth of water plus the degree of dilution by land-derived muds.

The variations were then accentuated by secondary processes. *Chondrites* is again helpful, for where the burrows are traced from less- into more-calcareous layers they also became noticeably more calcareous, ie the burrows were made, then also affected by the secondary drawing together of the calcium-rich layers.

BLACK VEN LANDSLIP

There is no direct coastal road from Lyme Regis to Charmouth nowadays due to the activity of Black Ven, the greatest landslip of the West Dorset coast. The cliff-top path provides magnificent views down over its terraces, mud-flows and swampy ground, and the remains of earlier roads across the area can be traced to their abrupt junctions with the slip faces. The first Lyme-Charmouth road through the area was built in 1825, suffering slip damage in 1828, 1832 and 1852. Damage became so serious by 1916 that warning signs were erected. A further movement occurred in 1922 and the road was closed in 1924 when a new, more inland route was constructed. This was also destroyed in 1963, but the present character of the landslip is the result of major falls in 1956–7 and 1958. The latter fall began on a February night. By morning a huge fan of debris 410m wide and crusted with uprooted trees had pushed across the beach, extending up to 91m seaward of the previous shore-line. The following day a large mass of Upper Greensand covered with bushes and trees was seen crawling down the edge of the highest terrace, while a river of mud flowed down to the shore.

Black Ven Cliffs

	Succession	Dip	Major Terraces
Cretaceous {	Upper Greensand		Base of Upper
	Gault Clay		Greensand
	UNCONFORMITY Plane dips 1°–2° S or SSW		
Lower	Green Ammonite Beds ⎫		Base of
	(east side only). ⎟		Belemnite
Jurassic	Belemnite Marls ⎬	Dipping 2°–3°	Marls
or Lias	Black Ven Marls ⎟	ESE	Base of Black
	Shales with Beef ⎭		Ven Marls

The upper terrace is due to the top of the hard Belemnite Marl which underlies the Cretaceous unconformity everywhere along the slip except on the east flank. There the ESE dip brings in a small thickness of Green Ammonite Beds. The middle and lower terraces are due to hard limestone bands. See page 34 for details of the Upper Greensand.

Many people visiting the Lyme-Charmouth area have visions of easy fossil spotting, ideas fuelled by what they have seen in museum displays, but the landslips are not a provident means of bringing higher beds down to the students' reach. They often hide more than they reveal. Prolific as the fauna is, a good collection in this area depends on years of patient work. A detailed knowledge of the succession must be acquired. The papers of Dr W. D. Lang testify to this (see Bibliography) and are invaluable to the understanding of the cliffs.

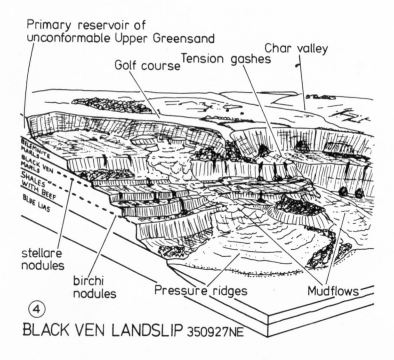

Primary reservoir of
unconformable Upper Greensand

Golf course Tension gashes

Char valley

BELEMNITE MARLS
BLACK VEN MARLS
SHALES WITH BEEF
BLUE LIAS

stellare
nodules

birchi
nodules

Pressure ridges

Mudflows

④

BLACK VEN LANDSLIP 350927NE

The landslips do provide access to the lower terraces and steps of Black Ven. The highest terrace can be reached from the cliff top via The Spittles on the west side. Note that more than three terraces occur—those indicated are the more laterally extensive flats. At the margins of the slips major steps sometimes combine.

The terrace at the base of the Black Ven Marl is formed by the *birchi* limestone nodules. Worked as cement-stones, these are often surrounded by 'beef' and contain well-preserved ammonites, *Microdoceras birchi*. The face then usually rises steeply through the Black Ven Marls to another similarly controlled terrace near their top, formed by the *stellare* nodules (*Asteroceras stellare*) and the Coinstone.

Even if access is impossible, other details of the Black Ven Marl sequence can be picked out visually from below. Thin limestones, known as the Lower Cement Bed and the Pavior, occur 12m and 16·5m respectively above the *birchi* nodules. Above these limestones minor lines of nodules, known as the Flatstones and the Woodstone, can be picked out. Above them again are two beds which, if located, may yield highly prized specimens—the pyritised pentacrinal crinoid *Extracrinus briareus* and a limestone crowded with ammonites, *Promicroceras planicosta* and *Amoeboceras*. Both are impersistent beds, but a superb specimen of the former is displayed in Barney's Fossil Exhibition in Charmouth, while the latter can be seen in Dorchester Museum and in a beautiful polished mantelpiece in the Sherborne Council Offices. All the beds in the top part of the Black Ven Marls above the *stellare* nodules are apt to be covered by talus falling from the Belemnite Marls above. Better exposures of the upper Black Ven Marls may be seen east of the River Char (Chapter 3).

The Belemnite Marls are much lighter in colour and more permeable. Their calcareous bands appear light grey but are not compacted as in the Blue Lias. As the name implies, belemnites are numerous in them. The staggering thing is that in some cases the squid-like creatures which surrounded these shells have been so well preserved that their ink sacs have remained. In 1836 Buckland stated that the ink had even been used to make sepia drawings—ink 190 million years old!

The reason why study of the Black Ven area is often difficult, despite the richness of the material, is the masking effect of the complex of rotational slides, sand-runs, and flows, mud slides and rock falls which scar the face of this 130m high cliff. Remember that the mechanisms are equally important inland as well, where water seeping from the Upper Greensand is the major cause (Chapter 11).

Figure 4 shows the causes of movement on Black Ven. Detailed study of the landslip by the Institute of Geological Sciences has led to the formation of a principle of general application, the reservoir principle. A permeable rock is the first requirement, one which can accept, retain and discharge ground water. To do this it must have an impermeable or less permeable bed below. It may then be capable of holding water to such an extent that it can discharge its flow into the unstable area without any seasonal control. The Upper Greensand is the local villain of the piece and the landslip suffers greatly, for this regular flow must be added to the damage caused by surface run-off. General weakening of the whole rock fabric results, increasing and regenerating the slip's unstable nature. Surface run-off and flow creates secondary reservoirs on the badly drained terraces, and well-developed secondary reservoirs can also be active at all seasons. Their marshy nature is easily seen from the top of Black Ven as one looks down on the top shelf. Notice that the basic form of the undercliff and toe areas is still controlled by the underlying succession, however. The whole business of failure is a near-surface process and actual rock falls are produced by the slipping of fragments of terrace edges rather than forward body movement of whole beds.

The slips provide photogenic examples of the various aspects of failure—tension cracks, rotational slides, over-saturated and swollen clays, pressure ridges, gullying, and a great variety of types of flow. Rotational slides are most evident in the Upper Greensand at the top. There, as described in the eye witness account above, large conical buttresses left between adjacent gullies fall whenever local shear stresses exceed the resistance of the poorly bonded, decalcified sands.

Having studied Black Ven the student should visit Barney's Fossil Exhibition at Charmouth. This will certainly inspire a second visit to Black Ven and the continued study of the sections east of the River Char.

CHAPTER 3

Jurassic of West Dorset Coast—2: Charmouth to Burton Bradstock

STONEBARROW CLIFFS AND THE BELEMNITE MARLS

Leaving the River Char, the cliffs are based on the Black Ven Marls, often nodular and septarian, and the important marker horizons are all limestones. Two are soon encountered: the Lower and Upper Cement Beds. The table below will help the explorer to locate his position in the rest of the Black Ven Marl succession. The vertical distances between the various limestones are given.

Succession of the upper part of the Black Ven Marls:

Hummocky Limestone—Base of the much lighter coloured Belemnite
                          Marls

1m interval of marls
Flinty limestone nodules

3m interval of marls
Watch Ammonite Stone—30cm thick, full of ammonites *Promicroceras*
                         planicosta and *Amoeboceras*

8m interval of marls
Oxynoticeras lymense bed—Well pyritised specimens of this ammonite
2m interval of marls   ⎰ Local erosional break with the lower and
←————————————— ⎨ middle *oxynotum* zone missing—these parts
Coinstone—limestone   ⎱ seen inland, however, Vale of Marshwood

1m interval of marls
Stellare nodules—15–30cm diameter, enclosing ammonites *Asteroceras*
                      stellare
2m interval of marls

Limestone with Brachiopods—25cm thick, full of silvery coarse ribbed
                         brachiopods. Weathers yellow in cliffs
7·5m interval of marls with occasional limestone nodules

Stonebarrow Flatstones—Secondary nodules with prominent bedding
         lines, containing ammonites *Asteroceras*
         obtusum with body chambers filled with
         brown calcite
1m interval of marls
Paper Shales—30cm of very thinly laminated shales
1m interval of marls
Upper Cement Bed (Pavior)—Discontinuous band of limestone.
         Reaches beach level 1·5km E of River
         Char mouth
5m interval of marls
Lower Cement Bed—First prominent and continuous one seen going E
Further 12m of Black Ven Marls below down to *birchi* Tabular Bed

The tabular impersistent Coinstone forms an interesting horizon. In places it is very damaged by boring organisms and there
are worm burrows encrusting the underside, ie the stone must have
stood as pedestals on the sea-floor during a break in deposition.
Confirmation is provided by the local absence of the lower and
middle parts of the succeeding *oxynotum* zone.

Fallen masses frequently obscure parts of the local cliffs, but
at low tide pockets of drifted and sorted pyritised ammonites may
be found. The problem, then, is to relate them to their true
horizons.

1·6km east of the Char lies Hawkfish Ledge, marking the Black
Ven Marls/Belemnite Marls boundary. The latter are much lighter
grey. It might be helpful to come here first and see the colour
contrast before studying the Black Ven landslip.

Immediately behind Hawkfish Ledge is the waterfall of Westhay
Water, a hanging valley. East of the fall, the banded Belemnite
Marls form low cliffs with their top bed, the Belemnite Stone, at
the top of the face. The beds are thrown into a gentle syncline
here and, by observing the Belemnite Stone at the top, it is possible
to detect several small faults which cut the structure. Their general
effect is to offset the rise of the beds on the far side of the syncline,
throwing the beds down east each time and thus keeping the
Belemnite Stone at the cliff top. The slickensided fault-planes can
be readily located. The syncline ends about 0·5km east where
Ridge Water trickles down the cliff.

Along the synclinal area the receding upper slopes are in the next Lias group, the Green Ammonite Beds. Luckily on the east side of the syncline two faults intersect just within the cliff face. Throwing the Belemnite Stone down 31m, well below beach level, they bring the intriguingly named Green Ammonite Beds down into the vertical lower cliff. These can be examined later after visiting the Stonebarrow landslips.

Though smaller in scale than Black Ven, these slips contain many interesting features. In the small failures near Westhay Water, splendid earth stacks stand as turf-capped columns while shear stresses have collapsed all the ground around them. Stonebarrow itself currently provides better examples of rotational slide blocks than Black Ven. Figure 5 shows the block of Cretaceous Upper Greensand with a World War II building on it, tilted and now subsided 21–24m into Fairy Dell.

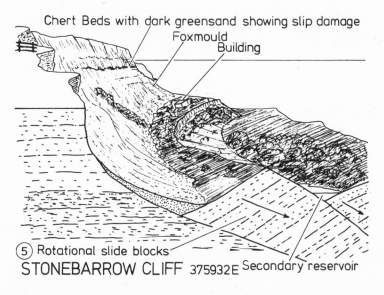

Chert Beds with dark greensand showing slip damage
Foxmould
Building

⑤ Rotational slide blocks
STONEBARROW CLIFF 375932E Secondary reservoir

Stonebarrow provides a good site to examine the Upper Greensand; it is described here rather than in the Cretaceous chapters since it forms such distinctive features on top of the West Dorset cliffs. The beds still *in situ* form a gentle slope which allows access in places. They are divided into Chert Beds, Foxmould and

Cowstones in descending order. None of them seems to be green on the weathered faces because the green glauconite mineral which earns them their name is a hydrous silicate of iron and becomes oxidised to the colour so aptly embodied in the name Golden Cap. The Chert Beds speak for themselves, layers of black-brown silica nodules, while the Foxmould is sandy and the Cowstones are sandy concretions. The difference between the last two is another example of a secondary process.

Calcium carbonate was formerly present in the Upper Greensand but it has now been dissolved out, leaving the beds loose and liable to failure. The lime mineral has been washed down through the sands and, with some dissolved silica from the Chert Beds, has formed the Cowstone concretions. They may be found on the terraces of Black Ven though they seem to be locally absent at Stonebarrow and Golden Cap.

This activity has affected the Upper Greensand fossils. Near the base and in the Cowstones they are preserved in calcium carbonate, but higher up in the decalcified beds of the Foxmould only the cavities which held the fossils are left. At the top, near the Chert Beds, these cavities have sometimes been refilled by silica, which seems to have particularly liked to replace oyster shells, eg *Exogyra, Pecten*. *Exogyra* is so common in the higher beds of the Upper Greensand that they are named the Exogyra Sandstones (Chapter 10). The most likely fossil discovered below Stonebarrow is the worm cast *Serpula concava*.

The succession seen in the back scar above Fairy Dell is:

Drift	6·0m	
Yellow coarse quartz sand	0·6m	
Chert Beds	9m	With a very noticeable 0·6m dark greensand in their middle (this is the most easily spotted horizon in the section)
Glauconitic sand	1·2m	With layers of *Exogyra* and broken *Pecten*
Foxmould	up to 30·5m	

THE GREEN AMMONITE BEDS

More marly than the Belemnite Marls, the Green Ammonite Beds do not contain any limestones of sufficient thickness to have been worked as cementstones, or to make resistant horizons. Consequently they usually form gentle slopes, often washed inland by the debris of Middle Lias beds which accumulates upon them, and only kept vertical in the coastal cliffs by the trimming action of the sea.

The notable feature of the Green Ammonite Beds is that they thin westwards, so an idea of their variations is essential before setting out. The reduction is fairly even throughout the succession and, as the table shows, occurs in the more shaley beds.

West						East
Stonebarrow	W of Fiary Dell	Westhay Water		Golden Cap		

Lowest Tier (lowest of the Three Tiers at the base of the Middle Lias)

	⌈ 3m of shales		⌈ 5·4m		⌈ 6m	
7·8m ⟨	Upper Limestone	11·8m ⟨	U.L.	16·6m ⟨	U.L.	
	⌊ 4·8m of shales		⌊ 6·4m		⌊ 10·6m	

——————————————Red Band——————————————

	⌈ 3·6m of shales		⌈ 6·4m		⌈ 10m	
6·9m ⟨	Lower Limestone	11·2m ⟨	L.L.	17m ⟨	L.L.	
	⌊ 3·3m of shales		⌊ 4·8m		⌊ 7m	
	Belemnite Stone below		B.S.		B.S.	

The Upper Limestone is in two beds separated by 1m of blue-grey clay. The Red Band consists of three thin calcareous sandstones and shales. Its name comes from the upper and lower of its calcareous layers, which weather reddish in colour. The Lower Limestone is nodular and discontinuous but fossils are most abundant near that level. The green calcite-filled chambers of *Androgynoceras lataecosta* which earn the beds their general name are enclosed inside nodules. Other fossils likely to be found are the ammonite *Tragophylloceras loscombi*, small spiral gastropods and crinoids in the Red Band, and plenty of belemnites near the Belemnite Stone below.

The beds can be examined in the degraded cliff tops while

walking over Stonebarrow. They thin westward, as shown in the table, eventually rising to be truncated by the Cretaceous unconformity. Occasional forays on to the receding upper cliffs can be made in safer spots. At Westhay Water all this upper slope is in Green Ammonite Beds, the outcrop of the Upper Limestone V-ing up valley at the level of the old limekiln on the west side, while the Red Band traverses the stream almost on the 30m contour. Three groups of ammonites may be searched for in the beds: the *lataecosta* group (*Androgynoceras lataecosta*) near the Lower Limestone, the *striatus* group in the Red Band, and the *oistoceras* group in and near the Upper Limestone. Pyritised ammonites and partly pyritised crinoid stems can be easily collected on the slipped hillwash, the latter brownish and easily mistaken for modern twigs until the cross section is washed clean and checked.

GOLDEN CAP

At 188m, Golden Cap is the highest cliff anywhere on the south coast. Its slopes steepen near the summit as the cherty heather-covered top is approached. The Upper Greensand capping can be examined on the east side of the weathered face but access is difficult. Most of the face is in the Foxmould, with about 4m of Chert Beds above. Descending the west side there are further excellent views of landslip phenomena. Once on the beach at St Gabriel's Mouth, examination of the Green Ammonite Beds cliff section can be resumed. Figure 2 shows the succession.

Immediately east of the mouth the beds are involved in a gentle anticline. This brings the Belemnite Stone up to beach level again, and it can be examined easily at the base of the cliffs between the mounds of fallen Green Ammonite material. The Red Band is close to the top of the cliff face in the anticline.

The Belemnite Stone falls below sea level again as the anticline gives way eastwards to a syncline below Golden Cap. Cross the toe of the slips just west of the headland and examine the vertical west face of Golden Cap. About 27m above the beach is the prominent overhang at the base of the Three Tiers. Falls may be too frequent for the middle and upper tiers of these three calcareous sandstone beds to be very obvious. They form the base of the Middle Lias, although the characteristic species of the ammonite *Amaltheus* of the Middle Lias actually appear first 3m lower, within the top part of the Green Ammonite Beds. The true junction does not show up well visually, however.

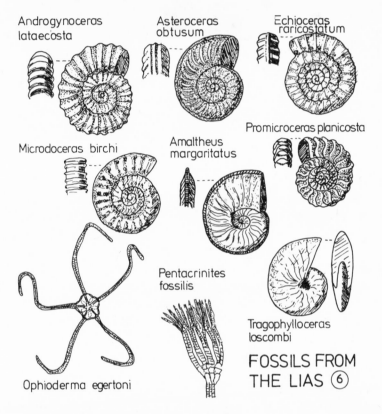

Androgynoceras lataecosta

Asteroceras obtusum

Echioceras raricostatum

Microdoceras birchi

Amaltheus margaritatus

Promicroceras planicosta

Pentacrinites fossilis

Tragophylloceras loscombi

Ophioderma egertoni

FOSSILS FROM THE LIAS ⑥

The sea keeps the cliff faces of Golden Cap trimmed vertically and fallen material on the shore may be from a variety of sources— Green Ammonite Beds of the lowest 27m, from the Three Tiers, or from the Eype Clay or Downcliff Sands above again. Nodules of iron pyrites are quite common, some of them quite large with rows of intergrown cubes. Detached but wave-damaged whorls of ammonites can be picked up, while others and nests of oyster shells are exposed in the shore reefs.

THORNCOMBE BEACON

The cliffs E of Seatown expose:

Bridport Sands
Down Cliff Clay
Junction Bed
Thorncombe Sands
Down Cliff Sands with Margaritatus Stone at top

	Starfish Bed	1·3m
	Marls & Shell Bed	1·2m
Eype Clay	Marls	17m
(given in	Sandstone	0·9m
greater detail)	Marl	0·45cm
	Eype Nodule Bed	45–60cm
	Clay	41m

(Three Tiers below)

The Eype Nodule Bed is the first to look for. Its outcrop is usually 5m above the Seatown beach level and is marked by a line of seepages. The nodules form two bands, 45–60cm apart, and though they are rarely over 75mm in diameter the calcareous lumps contain many fragments of ammonites, including *Tragophylloceras loscombi*, *Amaltheus stokesi*, *Amaltheus compressus* and *Leptaeloceras aff. pseudo-radians*.

Measuring the section with the additional details from the table, locate the top of the Eype Clay. Further interesting fossil beds occur at that horizon. The top bed of the clay is a 1·3m sandstone (the paradox arises because sets of beds are named after their dominant rock character!). The bed is greenish grey, micaceous and calcareous, and rather crumbly when weathered. It can be identified in the cliffs by the strong line of springs thrown out at its base—a feature also useful in locating it inland when there is no exposure. The spring line is quite low down on the cliffs at Thorncombe Beacon and may be covered in the debris.

On the flat base of the bed are the abundant and much sought after remains of the brittle starfish, *Ophioderma egertoni* (Figure 6). Great care is needed to remove one from the crumbly sandstones which must be chiselled well away from the specimen itself. Many are found complete, but slabs covered with segments of limbs also occur.

The rest of the Middle Lias must be largely studied from fallen blocks. Figure 7 shows the face of Thorncombe Beacon. The Eype Clay is succeeded by the Down Cliff Sands, grey and silty at first, becoming sandy and brown above with the Margaritatus Stone at the top. About 30cm thick, the stone is a blue-centred, yellow-weathering limestone. It yields *Amaltheus margaritatus*, obtainable from fallen blocks. In the face its horizon can be located by the 2m of clay above it since this produces a second noticeable line of seepages.

From the shore, it is difficult to appreciate how much the different beds of the Middle Lias vary in thickness, or that they form a broad anticline in these cliffs. The geologist who successfully measures and examines such an area must also be a mountaineer. Sedimentation did not take place in an unbroken sequence. Many beds were eroded again shortly after deposition, action bound to vary their thickness, continuity and other features. The most remarkable bed in these respects is the Junction Bed—Starfish Bed apart, the most fascinating material seen here.

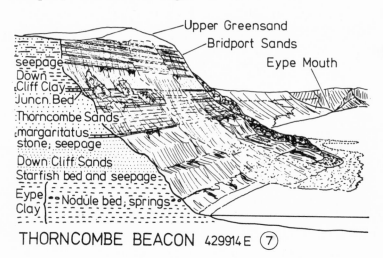

THORNCOMBE BEACON 429914 E (7)

THE JUNCTION BED

The Junction Bed has a distinctive appearance, multicoloured and conglomeratic, a mixture of pink, red, brown, yellow, crowded with fossils, but its importance is that its 0·75–1·3m provide one of the best examples of a condensed sequence anywhere in the stratigraphical record. One Middle Lias and at least four Upper Lias zones are represented in the Junction Bed. While this thin miniature record was being deposited here in Dorset at least 105m of strata were formed in Yorkshire!

The answer to the origin of this very special bed takes us back to Chapter 1. The changing pattern of basins and rising fold axes of Jurassic times meant that great thicknesses of rocks could accumulate in some areas. Others, situated on submarine ridges, received very little sediment. For every 3m formed in Yorkshire at this time less than 4·5cm were deposited in Dorset—but the ammonite faunas of the time were the same in both districts.

Here is ample proof of the value of the rapidly evolving and widespread ammonites as zone fossils. Some of the assemblages spread through 105m of Yorkshire strata are concentrated in 0·75–1·3m in Dorset, while others are missing altogether due to local erosion over the submarine ridge. The Dorset Junction Bed is still rich in their remains, but not jammed solid. It contains a spaced sequence, as notable for its gaps as it is for its contents.

Proof of slow accumulation over a long period and of the erosional activity taking place at times is found in the fact that in some layers ammonites which were buried on edge have been cut in half, while others lying flat to the sea bed have been sectioned—accurately sliced in two. The various layers clearly had ample time to solidify and be eroded before the next part was deposited. Some of the fallen blocks display these unconformities in quite small samples. Most of the material in these blocks is from the Upper Lias part of the Junction Bed. The one Middle Lias member, the more yellowish-brown Marlstone Rock Bed, is less frequently found.

The Junction Bed succession here at the coast:

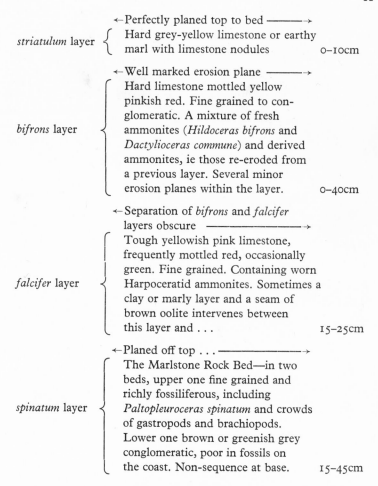

striatulum layer
←Perfectly planed top to bed ────→
Hard grey-yellow limestone or earthy
marl with limestone nodules   0–10cm

bifrons layer
←Well marked erosion plane ────→
Hard limestone mottled yellow
pinkish red. Fine grained to conglomeratic. A mixture of fresh
ammonites (*Hildoceras bifrons* and
Dactylioceras commune) and derived
ammonites, ie those re-eroded from
a previous layer. Several minor
erosion planes within the layer.   0–40cm

falcifer layer
←Separation of *bifrons* and *falcifer*
layers obscure ────→
Tough yellowish pink limestone,
frequently mottled red, occasionally
green. Fine grained. Containing worn
Harpoceratid ammonites. Sometimes a
clay or marly layer and a seam of
brown oolite intervenes between
this layer and . . .   15–25cm

spinatum layer
←Planed off top . . . ────→
The Marlstone Rock Bed—in two
beds, upper one fine grained and
richly fossiliferous, including
Paltopleuroceras spinatum and crowds
of gastropods and brachiopods.
Lower one brown or greenish grey
conglomeratic, poor in fossils on
the coast. Non-sequence at base.   15–45cm

THE EYPE MOUTH FAULT

A short distance east of Eype Mouth the Middle and Upper Lias beds are involved in the Eype Mouth Fault which has a downthrow of 180–210m. Like the Abbotsbury Fault it is one of the major pre-Cretaceous disturbances in Dorset.

Ascending the cliff east of Eype Mouth, the path and cliff face trend away diagonally inland. If the whole face was visible below it would be seen to expose the Eype Clay and Starfish Bed just east of the mouth, followed in upward order by the rest of the Middle Lias, the Junction Bed where present, and Bridport Sands at the top. However, the lower cliff face is obscured by land-slipped material. Deceptively coloured by yellow weathered wash from the cliff face, this fallen area is in fact foundered Fullers Earth and Forest Marble from the opposite or downthrown side of the fault. The cliff face and fault plane are practically parallel, so as you walk up the path you are following the fault line. The cliff has hardly receded at all on this 'fixed' side of the fault line, but on the seaward side the downthrown Fullers Earth and Forest Marble have totally collapsed. They were left in a narrow tongue between the converging courses of the fault and the original cliff line—and foundered as a result.

Eventually the path reaches a point where the cliff face turns abruptly seawards and the grey-coloured beds on the downthrown side are still in position. The spot is known as Fault Corner and the fault plane can be seen in it. The course of the fault can then be

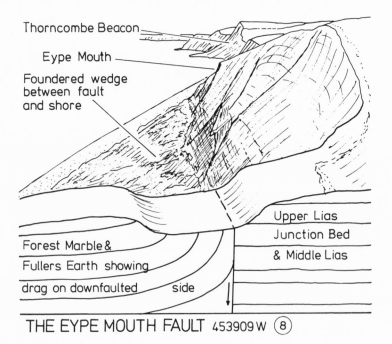

Thorncombe Beacon

Eype Mouth

Foundered wedge between fault and shore

Upper Lias

Junction Bed

Forest Marble & Fullers Earth showing drag on downfaulted side

& Middle Lias

THE EYPE MOUTH FAULT 453909 W (8)

traced inland as a depression followed by the path, past an old limekiln and over into the Brit Valley.

With the exception of the Cretaceous unconformity, the Eype Mouth Fault forces the student to make a jump in the strati-graphical record for the first time since leaving Lyme Regis. The Bridport Sands and Inferior Oolite must be omitted for the time, although they outcrop to the east, and the cliff sections to Bridport Harbour continued in the Middle Jurassic Fullers Earth and Forest Marble. Features of these beds are described in the next chapter.

EAST CLIFF AND BURTON CLIFF

East of Bridport Harbour there are two splendid cliffs of golden sands, with regular horizontal ribbing which could have easily inspired a cathedral architect. The ribbing in these Bridport Sands (Upper Lias) is due to some beds having a higher calcareous content, ie a natural cement. The sands are remarkably uniform in character and grain size, and do in fact span the boundary between the Lias and the Middle Jurassic. They are known else-where as the Yeovil Sands and as the Midford Sands around Bath. They form the scarp slope of the Cotswold Hills, where they rise from the Marlstone shelf, referred to earlier, to the Inferior Oolite capping the dipslope.

While the Junction Bed is a superb example of a condensed sequence, the Bridport Sands are diachronous—small wonder Dorset is such a geological training ground. Ammonite faunas show that the sands cut time boundaries. In Upper Lias times they had already formed and been followed by the Inferior Oolite limestones in the Cotswolds, while in Dorset deposition was still of the mainly clayey Lias character. Sand formation only spread into Dorset at the very end of Upper Lias times, and then it con-tinued late, delaying the appearance of the conditions associated with the Inferior Oolite (Figure 9).

At a first glance Burton Cliff seems identical to East Cliff. However, about 155m east of the river a fault downthrowing eastward cuts the cliff, dropping the Inferior Oolite capping sufficiently to bring in the Fullers Earth again in a cliff top outcrop (Figure 9). Blocks of Inferior Oolite have fallen to the beach beyond the fault and provide the best exposures of these beds, since most of the inland quarry outcrops where they were once worked extensively are now overgrown.

The Burton Cliff Section, Inferior Oolite.

Quarry Bed

Fullers Earth Clay. — 61cm seen.

Top Beds or Upper Inferior Oolite

- Blue centred nodular limestone; *Parkinsonia*, *Belemnopsis*, lamellibranchs and gastropods. — 15cm — FIRST
- Massive limestone. — 63cm — SECOND
- Sponge Beds: Marl with two limestone partings crowded with sponges, *Clypeus*, brachiopods, lamellibranchs. — 35·5cm
- Rubbly limestone with similar fossils, including large Nautili. — 40·5cm
- Blue Grey limestone, rubbly top, attached serpulids, *Sphaeroidothyris sphaeroidalis*, *Clypeus*, lamellibranchs. — 56cm — THIRD
- *Astarte 'obliqua'* Bed; crumbly brown ironshot limestone crowded with fossils. — 10cm
- Conglomerate of ironshot rock, patchily present poorly preserved ammonites.

Top Beds above rest on different beds in different places, so beds below were raised and gently folded before Top Beds were formed.

Middle Inferior Oolite

- The Red Bed; Hard, grey crystalline limestone, level eroded top. — 56cm — FOURTH
- Limestone with brownish limonitic granules. — 18cm
- Limestone, bluish, limonitic ooliths and large limonitic concretions near the base; The Snuff Boxes. — 7·5cm

Lower Inferior Oolite

- Yellow Conglomerate Bed: with rolled fossils from re-eroded earlier beds. — 4cm

Scissum or Bottom Bed: = top of 30m of Bridport Sands extending down to base of cliff.

Note that quarrymens' numbers are the reverse of the order of formation. Several fallen blocks of different thicknesses rest on the beach. The most distinctive bed is the Snuff Boxes, a layer of large oval limonitic concretions from which the position of the beds in the blocks can be worked out. The largest currently present extends from the Snuff Boxes almost up to the Sponge Beds.

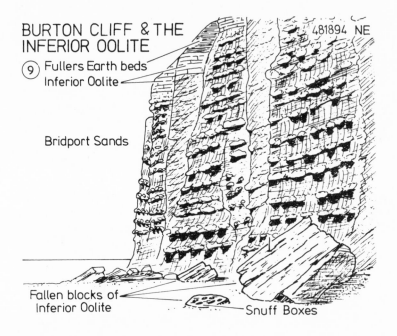

BURTON CLIFF & THE INFERIOR OOLITE

481894 NE

(9) Fullers Earth beds
Inferior Oolite

Bridport Sands

Fallen blocks of Inferior Oolite

Snuff Boxes

The total thickness of the Inferior Oolite here, 4m, is another example of a condensed sequence. Like the Junction Bed example, the Inferior Oolite is also full of non-sequences, some of them of local significance, others representing more widespread intervals of erosion. The best major example is the unconformity between the Middle and Upper Beds. Recalling the succession studied from the earliest Jurassic beds at Lyme Regis, this is the first major break in deposition since the beginning of Jurassic time. What is its significance and would it have been better to give different names to the beds above and below it rather than call them all Inferior Oolite?

The cause was renewed movement along old Hercynian folds, originally created at the close of Carboniferous times. Affecting the Devonian and Carboniferous rocks of Devon and Cornwall, their eastward extension provided an important part of the geological basement of Dorset. The Jurassic sediments accumulated on this, so when the old folds stirred slightly again in the midst of the locally thin and condensed Inferior Oolite deposition, the slight movements had some very marked effects. Some areas were pushed up above sea level and their deposits immediately eroded away again. The eroded fossils were sometimes reburied in other layers, ie became derived fossils. In contrast much thicker quantities of a particular bed could accumulate in downwarped localities.

It is perhaps unfortunate that the name Inferior Oolite spans this important break. It was a tempting trap for early geologists because the whole series has such a similar lithology, and contrasts markedly with both the preceding Bridport Sands and the Fullers Earth which followed.

The succession is not complete anywhere in the country, but in comparison with the 90m of Lower and Middle Inferior Oolite alone at Cheltenham, the Dorset area is certainly condensed! There is a good deal of variation within Dorset—the 63cm limestone near the top in Burton Cliff increases to 1·45m at Burton Broadstock and 4·5m at Chideock (page 139). Around Sherborne in North Dorset the Top Beds include the famous Sherborne Building Stone, 3–7m thick. The general thinning southwards throughout Dorset is interpreted as thinning against the flanks of an already active Weymouth-Purbeck anticlinal structure.

CHAPTER 4

The Weymouth Lowland

The Weymouth Lowland lies south of a line from Abbotsbury to Osmington. Its northern boundary is overlooked by steep slopes of Upper Greensand and Chalk, forming the faulted margin of the Dorset Downs here and providing fine viewpoints across the lowland to the Isle of Portland. The lowland is in fact an eroded much-faulted anticline of Jurassic Beds. If the Cretaceous which bounds it ever covered it, all trace of this has been destroyed. True to its anticlinal form the oldest beds outcrop near the centre of the eroded structure, in this case the Fullers Earth. The lowland enables the student to continue the chronological sequence of Dorset deposition from the Fullers Earth up to the Kimmeridge Clay and Portland Beds. It is a fascinating district despite the problems of numerous strike faults and low cliff faces—the latter due to the protective influence of Chesil Beach on the west coast. On the east shore there is much marshy ground caused by the curving outcrop of the Oxford Clays as the anticline plunges eastwards. There built-up land combines with Radipole Lake and Lodmoor to obscure most of the beds. The most important faults of the district are those on its northern boundary (Chapter 15).

The Fullers Earth and Forest Marble belong to the Great Oolite Series, and were formed during changeable conditions, posing problems for geologists correlating the deposits from different areas. The Forest Marble, for example, is the equivalent of a much thicker series of limestone beds in outcrops north of the Bath-Mendips region. Similarly the Fullers Earth is much more clayey in Dorset than farther north where it contains important stone beds. Hence the name Great Oolite series, given to the two formations, was not earned in Dorset! It is also worth noting that the Cornbrash is at its thickest in Dorset, 7·5–9m, while the

Corallian is so poorly endowed with corals here that it hardly merits the name.

In Figure 10 notice how the outcrops appear north and south of the anticlinal axis in the west, but close to the east as the upfold plunges underground. Like the Purbeck anticline the structure is not symmetrical. The northern limb is steep, giving only narrow outcrops of the Portland Sands and Stone on the slopes below the Cretaceous unconformity, while the southern limb is represented by the long gentle slope of the Isle of Portland (Chapter 6).

THE WEYMOUTH ANTICLINE ⑩

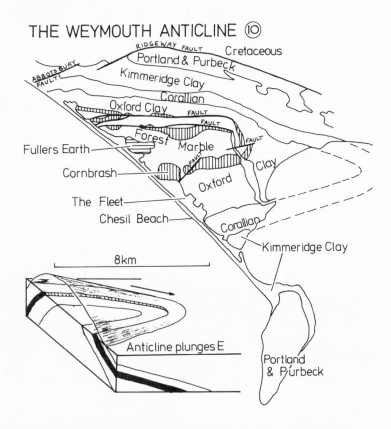

(*Generalised from maps of the Institute of Geological Sciences with permission of the Director*)

LANGTON HERRING AND HERBURY

Attractive Langton Herring makes an excellent centre when studying the lowest beds of the anticline. A 5km walk takes in all the exposures. Shorter itineraries are easily arranged. Take the no through road from Lower Farm, then the field path to Rodden Brook which can be crossed north by a little bridge hidden in the hedgerows. From Rodden Hive Bay walk west and north to Rodden Hive Point where the low cliff exposes a Fullers Earth lumachelle or shell bed. It is crowded with *Ostrea hebridica* and its variety *elongata*. Only part of the 6m bed is seen here but it forms an easily mapped feature everywhere, readily recognised in ploughed fields. Beneath it 1m of blue clay contains beautifully preserved fossils, including *Trigonia*. These weather out on the shore but fragments are more common than whole specimens.

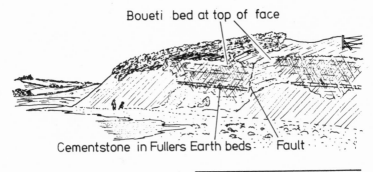

Boueti bed at top of face

Cementstone in Fullers Earth beds   Fault

NORTH SIDE OF HERBURY (11)
611811 ENE

Goniorhynchia boueti

Due to faulting, the oyster bed is seen again to the south. Return to the stream and cross south over the main axis of the anticline to Langton Hive Point below the coastguard cottages. Here a greater thickness is visible and a further outcrop can be detected about half-way along to the next bay south. Continue right round this bay to Herbury Point (Figure 11).

By working south, the explorer now moves up the succession to the Forest Marble. Herbury's northern cliff face is mainly Fullers Earth with a strong cementstone half-way up, but at the top is the crumbly weathering base of the Forest Marble. It can be reached at most points along the face, or where it descends west to the shore. Full of the heavily ribbed brachiopod *Goniorhynchia boueti* and the smoother shelled *Ornithella digona*, the bed is known as the *boueti* bed. The fossils can often be collected loose, fallen to the beach, or in the field above, and the bed is also rich in *Chlamys* valves, *Ostrea* and minute ostracods (see page 90). Some of the shells are encrusted with bryozoa, net-like colonial organisms. Higher beds of the Forest Marble follow to the south, the more typical golden limestones filled with silvery blue shell fragments.

Omitting the Cornbrash exposures around East Fleet, the Oxford Clay (Figure 12) provides a fine opportunity for the study of fossil zones.

Corallian Beds above

	Cardioceras cordatum	at 647777	
	Quenstedtoceras mariae	at 646784, S side of Tidmoor Cove	
	Quenstedtoceras lamberti	at 642786 Tidmoor Point shore behind rifle range	the most instruc-
	Peltoceras athleta *Erymnoceras coronatum*	at Crook Hill Brickpits, formerlyWebb & Major's on main road behind Amey Premix plant	tive zones locally
Oxford Clay	*Kosmoceras jason*	Poorly exposed. Outcrops N side of Chickerell Hive Point, in S part of Putton Lane Brickpit now a water lily farm	
	Sigalloceras calloviense	Poorly exposed, N end Putton Lane Brickpit	
	Proplanulites koenigi	Outcrops on shore 0·4km S of East Fleet Church; poorly exposed, N end Putton Lane Brickpit	

Cornbrash below

CROOK HILL BRICKPIT, CHICKERELL

This is another famous locality of the Weymouth area, yielding ammonites, turreted gastropods, lamellibranchs, septarian nodules and the crystalline form of gypsum, the mineral selenite.

Crook Hill Brickyard was opened by 1851 and made bricks, tiles, drain pipes, pottery and stoneware. Between 1907 and 1911 the pit was taken over by Webb and Major, hence the many references to this name in geological literature. Until 1940 the firm worked it in conjunction with pits at Broadmayne (Chapter 14). The pits eventually covered nearly 1·2 hectares, 27m depth towards Crook Hill itself, and were being extended westwards when the works closed in 1969. Although grey, buff and yellow in colour, the Oxford Clay fired to red or orange, as the cottages and chimney stacks testify. The latter are a good landmark since the pit is now effectively hidden behind the Amey Premix plant in its outer yard.

The workings are in two sections. In the smaller northern one many septarian nodules can be seen, but the most interesting feature is a large cementstone one lying left the entrance and full of crushed *Meleagrinella* and *Protocardia*. The northern area is in the *coronatum* zone (it is customary to refer to zones by the second part of the fossil name) which totals 9m of beds and forms the dividing spur between the two areas of the pit as well as the vertical face immediately north-west of the pond. Here and around the dividing spur the crushed ammonite *Kosmoceras*, the gastropod *Procerithium* and fossil wood can be found. The student will soon notice, however, that the fossils are generally flattened internal casts. This is because the Oxford Clay is rich in pyrite, seen weathering out as yellow crusts. Conditions during formation were similar to those of the Lias. The fossil shells have disappeared because ground water acting on the iron sulphide or pyrite material forms weak sulphuric acid from it. This attacks the calcium carbonate of the shells, dissolving them and forming calcium sulphate, ie gypsum, which is deposited in crystalline form as the mineral selenite. The pits are famous for their clear glassy intergrowths of this mineral.

The main pit is in the *athleta* zone, the top of its west face a marvellous vantage point over the area. The Cretaceous downs can be seen to the north and to the north-east in the cliffs of White Nothe, while Tidmoor Point and The Fleet are spread out below to the south-west. The far south-west end of the pit is the best area for selenite. Thick crusts of it enclose the septarian nodules there, the myriad smaller needles surrounded by soft white gypsum. Certain dark clay bands yield growths large enough to cover the palm of the hand, but remember the softness of gypsum when preparing these specimens. Careful handling is necessary to avoid scratching them.

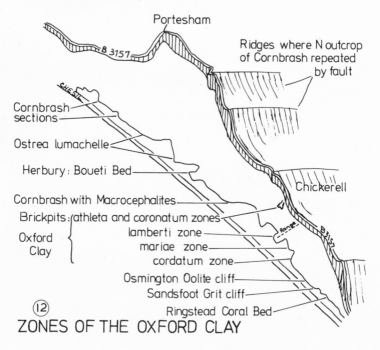

ZONES OF THE OXFORD CLAY

TIDMOOR POINT AND FURZEDOWN CLIFF

Return along the road to Weymouth and park in the lay-by opposite Cerne Villa Caravan Park. Walk on past the main gate to the rifle range and, unless the red flag is flying, take the farm lane which leads down its south-east boundary. This brings the student to the Fleet shore at Tidmoor Cove. Walk west and north to get behind the rifle range at Tidmoor Point. Over the years this area has been the most fruitful part of the *lamberti* zone. Specimens are small, however, and the only way to study them is to kneel on the shore and search very patiently. Many of the fossils are formed in reddish limonitic material, especially the tack-sized *Procerithium,* but well-pyritised ammonites occur. The most likely discoveries are plentiful small belemnites, but with care the ammonites *Kosmoceras* and *Quenstedtoceras* (Figure 13) will be

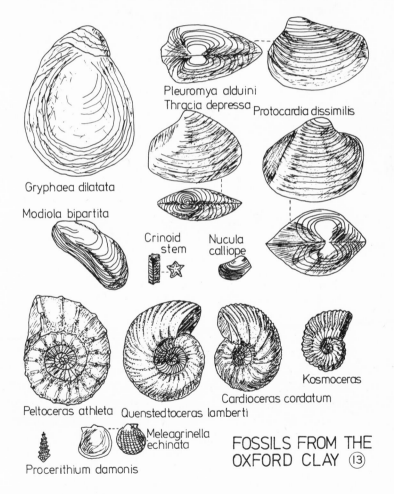

Pleuromya alduini

Thracia depressa

Protocardia dissimilis

Gryphaea dilatata

Modiola bipartita

Crinoid stem

Nucula calliope

Kosmoceras

Cardioceras cordatum

Peltoceras athleta

Quenstedtoceras lamberti

Meleagrinella echinata

Procerithium damonis

FOSSILS FROM THE OXFORD CLAY ⑬

found and single or short rows of ossicles from crinoid stems. Nearly fifty varieties of ammonites are recorded from this zone.

Tidmoor Point sets the tone for the rest of the Fleet shore study —very much a hands-and-knees affair. Return to Tidmoor Cove and walk south for about 100m where close examination of the *mariae* zone will reveal *Quenstedtoceras* again and *Cardioceras* species. There are fewer ammonite varieties in this zone. *Pentacrinus* crinoid ossicles occur again and small examples of the oysters *Gryphaea lituola* and *Gryphaea dilatata* (Figure 13).

Continue round the next bay past Littlesea Caravan Park and approach The Fleet's narrows west of Wyke Regis. Notice the well-developed seepage cans opposite on Chesil Beach (page 185). At 647777 the *cordatum* zone study begins. The shore is covered with rust-coloured nodules weathering out of the clays and earning this horizon the name Red Nodule Beds. Look at the nodules carefully for some are fossil casts—the elegantly curved lamellibranch *Modiola bipartita,* also *Thracia depressa* and *Pleuromya alduini. Gryphaea lituola* specimens are larger here and the heavily ribbed oyster *Lopha gregarea* appears. Shortly after leaving the *cordatum* zone the Oxford Clay gives way to the overlying Corallian with large doggers of Nothe Grit and the path is diverted inland around the army camp.

WYKE REGIS AND SANDSFOOT

The Corallian outcrop crosses the neck of land around Wyke Regis to Sandsfoot Castle and The Nothe on the north shores of Portland Harbour. Do not confuse The Nothe with White Nothe, the great chalk cliff east of Ringstead Bay (page 118). Much of The Nothe–Bencliffe area has been covered by buildings and public gardens, however, and the best coastal sections of the Corallian are along The Fleet west of Wyke Regis, and at Osmington Mills and Bran Point (Chapter 9). By car, access to the Wyke Regis section is better from the south end. Park at 662770 and cross the pathfields south-west from Martleaves Farm.

The Corallian Beds are dominated by clays, sands and oolitic limestones. Their sequence reveals a cyclic pattern:

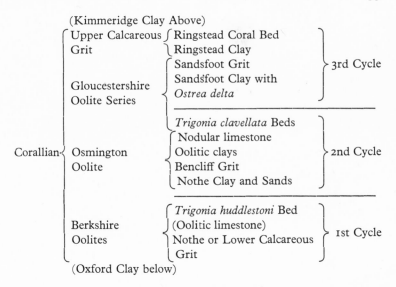

(Kimmeridge Clay Above)

Corallian

- Upper Calcareous Grit — { Ringstead Coral Bed / Ringstead Clay } ⎫
- Gloucestershire Oolite Series — { Sandsfoot Grit / Sandsfoot Clay with *Ostrea delta* } ⎬ 3rd Cycle
- Osmington Oolite — { *Trigonia clavellata* Beds / Nodular limestone / Oolitic clays / Bencliff Grit / Nothe Clay and Sands } ⎬ 2nd Cycle
- Berkshire Oolites — { *Trigonia huddlestoni* Bed / (Oolitic limestone) / Nothe or Lower Calcareous Grit } ⎬ 1st Cycle

(Oxford Clay below)

All these sediments formed during a shallow-water interval between the muds of the Oxford and Kimmeridge Clays but, as the table shows, there were two Corallian returns to muddy conditions. In the first, the Nothe Clay, the rounded *Gryphaea dilatata* of Oxford Clay times was still the oyster of the sea bed; but, by the second, the Sandsfoot Clay, *Ostrea delta*, had appeared. The latter is a flatter oyster, typically found in the ensuing Kimmeridge Clay. A characteristic of the Corallian is the absence of ammonites until the Ringstead Coral Bed at the top is reached.

Walk up to the north end near the army boat-training camp to follow the order of deposition. The oolitic limestones and grits form the highest cliffs seen since Herbury; the clays are eroded into bays and poorly exposed as a result. South of the camp a 4·5m cliff extends for 0·8km, the south dip enabling it to reveal 15m of Osmington Oolite and *Trigonia clavellata* Beds, becoming more fossiliferous in the top nodular rubble bed of the oolite and the 30cm of *Trigonia clavellata* Chief Shell Beds present. Compared to their 1m at Bran Point, the latter are not well represented in this section, but another local opportunity to examine them occurs in Sandsfoot Cove, see below. On reaching the path up to Mart-

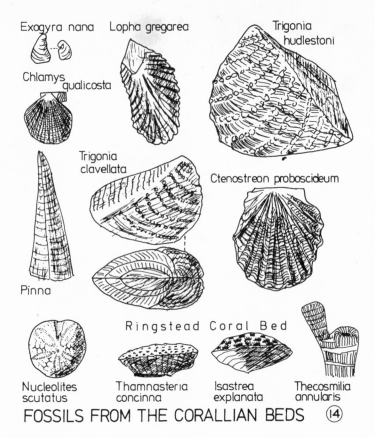

Exogyra nana   Lopha gregarea   Trigonia hudlestoni

Chlamys qualicosta

Trigonia clavellata

Ctenostreon proboscideum

Pinna

Ringstead Coral Bed

Nucleolites scutatus   Thamnasteria concinna   Isastrea explanata   Thecosmilia annularis

FOSSILS FROM THE CORALLIAN BEDS   (14)

leaves Farm continue a short distance south into the next bay and examine the cliff at 662766 close to the nearest electricity pole in the field above. Here the Ringstead Coral Bed outcrops, with typical grey-coloured Kimmeridge Clay beyond. The Coral Bed marks the top of the 3rd cycle but its limited coral contents represent only the swiftly migrating forms. The fauna of the bed is rich in serpulids, pectens and sea-urchin spines, however. Ammonites also reappear. Commonest among the weathered specimens on the shore are corrugated heavy shells of the pecten *Ctenostreon proboscideum* and masses of calcareous worm burrows, the grotesquely twisted *Serpula intestinalis*.

Moving inland, follow the strike of the beds across to the north

shore of Portland Harbour at Sandsfoot Castle Cove. The castle
on the west side dates from the 1540s and has been gradually
falling into the sea due to coast erosion. The rate of undermining
has slowed down since Portland Harbour breakwaters were constructed, 1847–72. However, the cliffs at the back of and east of
Castle Cove are still slipping, being in the weak Sandsfoot Clays.
At their base beyond the dinghy park is a good exposure of the
Trigonia clavellata Chief Shell Bed, absolutely crowded with
bivalves. They are difficult to extract.

The cliffs beneath the castle form the best Dorset exposure of
the Sandsfoot Grits, but it is not an easy area to study because of
the large fallen blocks, debris from the castle and the fact that
some of the grit beds pass into clays as they are traced under the
headland. The blue-brown clays contrast sharply with the rough
red-brown and gingery coloured grits. An impressive feature of
the latter are the jumbles of large Y-shaped burrows all through
the blocks. A scramble west around the headland will confirm two
oysters as the most common fossils—again the heavily ribbed
Ctenostreon proboscideum while, below the private beach paths,
a long narrow oyster, named *Pinna sandsfootensis* from the locality,
weathers grey amid the red-brown grits. On the west side of the
headland, the Ringstead Waxy Clays outcrop near the slipway and
the slumped cliff beyond contains the east end of the Coral Bed
and Kimmeridge Clay outcrops.

It would be convenient to study the Isle of Portland next but for
the fact that the Kimmeridge Clay is so poorly exposed in this area.
It is the reason for the separation of the island, the outcrop being
eroded to form Portland Roads. So we must head for Kimmeridge
Bay to continue the chronological sequence. First, however, the
student should return north across the Weymouth lowland to
examine the Abbotsbury iron ore.

Crossing north over the Weymouth lowland, the limestones
form sharp scarps or strike-faulted east-west ridges, eg at Wyke
Regis (Corallian) or at East Fleet (Cornbrash). Chickerell village
stands on the Cornbrash dip slope and the road east to Nottington
follows its crest for some distance.

Shortly after the elbow bend at the East Fleet junction the road runs straight for 1·6km. A small undulation in the descent to the Victoria Inn marks the outcrop of the *boueti* bed (base of Forest Marble) and around the inn the Fullers Earth oyster bed appears. Farther north beyond Bagwell Farm the route undulates due to strike faults repeating the northern outcrops of the Cornbrash and Forest Marble. Strong east-west ridges result, extending from Buckland Ripers to Langton Herring, and the presence of limestone is confirmed by old limekilns. The last repetition of the Cornbrash is quite a hogsback.

ABBOTSBURY IRON ORE

Around Abbotsbury the base of the Kimmeridge Clay outcrop is marked by an iron ore development. A small synclinal structure causes the beds to dip under the village from north, west and south. *Rasenia* species ammonites found in it confirm that the iron ore is a sedimentary deposit. Gingery-brown, oolitic, filled with grains as well as thin concretionary beds of hematite, the iron ore is difficult to distinguish from the ferruginous Sandsfoot Grits beneath it. The memory of the cliff colours below Sandsfoot Castle will confirm the problem. There is a lot of silica in the ooliths and, if these are sorted out from the rock, split and magnified, their dark reddish-black iron is seen to be only a crust. Within there is poorer-grade, powdery brown limonite. Although the iron content as a whole is over 30 per cent, the high silica content has always made the ore unprofitable.

The origin of sedimentary iron ores still poses problems. The most likely source here was derivation from erosion of a land area with a warm humid climate. The clear water conditions of the preceding Corallian confirm that little other sediment was being produced from this land. Deep weathering and solution provided the iron which was carried seawards, any ferrous iron within it being oxidised on arrival and deposited on the sea-bed. There the sifting action of gentle currents rolled sandgrains around, coating them with iron.

There are three sites where the ore can be examined. Park near the square 577854 in the centre of Abbotsbury. West of the school is Red Lane, often referred to as Folly Hollow. Walking up past the few cottages, keep right, up to a field gate. From the gate a site high up across the fields can be seen. It is crowned by a fir copse but best reached by another route (described below). For the moment turn left at the gate and down a short steep path to the stream. Cross the stream to the exposure on the west side (575854), where the beds are full of hematite grains. To visit the higher exposure, 577856, walk east from the square and in about 180m turn left up a bridlepath which leads directly to it. Ammonites occasionally weather out on the face but are not common at either site, no doubt because of the number of visitors to them. A third exposure occurs in the lane to Abbotsbury Gardens, 360m west of its junction with the B3157.

CHAPTER 5

Isle of Purbeck: South Coast

It is invidious to compare the many landscapes of Dorset. Never-theless the Isle of Purbeck holds a special place in most people's affections. Hidden south of a barrier of sparsely populated heath-lands and high chalk downlands, it has been able to maintain its secret charm. Even the exploitation of its building stones and 'marble' has not ravaged its appearance. In contrast to the open quarries of Portland, much of the working here was in cliff-face galleries. If anything, these now deserted caverns add to the dist-rict's mystique.

Coming from Weymouth the student will probably enter Pur-beck from East Lulworth, over Whiteways Hill, a fine structural introduction to Purbeck (see Chapter 12). With beds ranging from Kimmeridgian to Cretaceous, the Isle is a fascinating area. There are building stones, shale oil and Kimmeridge 'Coal', while in the Purbeck Beds, for which it is the type locality, there are forest, fish and insect beds, pond snails, ostracods, mammals, dinosaur tracks and many other fossils. To follow the time order, make first for Kimmeridge Bay, passing en route the inland features de-scribed on page 114.

CLAYS OIL AND SHALE

Although the Kimmeridge Clay consists mainly of black shales and clays, a generally unresistant formation, it also has some more resistant limestones which form the stone bands of the famous Kimmeridge ledges and break much of the wave force before it reaches the cliffs. Cause of numerous shipwrecks, each band is individually named (Figure 16). They act as useful markers in the succession.

Kimmeridge Bay can be off-putting at first. Eroded black shales discolour the seawater while their bituminous content gives the bay a peculiar odour, at its strongest in warm weather. Walk first to the north-west of the beach to view the working oil well. Sunk in 1959, it has nothing to do with the Kimmeridge Oil-shale, however. The base of the Kimmeridge Clays lies 200m below the surface here. Corallian Beds then extend down to 560m below surface and it is from the Cornbrash beneath them again that the well obtains 16,000 tonnes of oil per year.

The long area of south dips towards Hounstout, combined with the coastal erosion, has meant that the Kimmeridge Oil-shale, or Blackstone as it is known, could be worked in two ways. Surface outcrops were used open-cast on the cliff tops but, where the dip took the beds too deep for this, adits were driven in from the cliff face.

Kimmeridge Oil-shale, 'Coal' or Blackstone is a bituminous oil-shale. Its surface outcrop reaches the coast at the Cuddle and it is then seen dipping east down the cliffs towards Clavells Hard. It can be seen for a further 180m beyond the Hard before it dips below sea level (Figure 15). Eighteenth-century archaeologists were puzzled by numerous discs of this shale, about the size of a pocket watch, which turned up in local excavations. One early theory that these were a form of money accounts for continuing references to Kimmeridge 'Coal' money, but it was soon recognised that these were the discarded discs of lathe work from the manufacture of Roman armlets. Fragments in various stages of completion reveal the production methods.

In a hand-cut 8 by 2cm slab, holes were drilled to take the lathe chuck and the piece was rounded. Then sharp flint implements cut into each side until an outer ring was severed from the disc. Smoothing of its inner edge completed the armlet. Other sites of this early industry were Gallows Gore, Povington and Blashen-well, and other important products were spindle whorls, cups, vases and even elaborately carved chair legs.

Kimmeridge 'Coal' gives off large quantities of ash and sul-phuretted hydrogen, but despite the obnoxious smell it was used as a household fuel from very early times. It curls up along its bedding laminations when exposed, has a conchoidal fracture and, as the geologist will soon find, is easily ignited. Spontaneous combustion occurred at Clavell's Hard in the summer of 1973, turning the joints of the rock into reddened clinker and endowing anyone who lingered in the area with a distinctive smell! See Burning Cliff, Holworth, page 114.

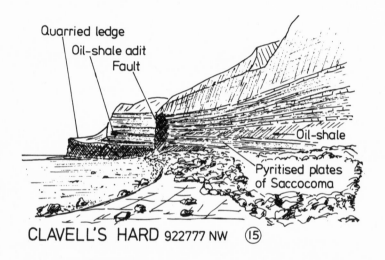

CLAVELL'S HARD 922777 NW (15)

The first use of Kimmeridge 'Coal' or Blackstone as an industrial fuel was in the seventeenth-century works of Sir William Clavell of nearby Smedmore House—hence the names Clavell Tower, Clavell's Hard. At first he used the beds both as a source of alum and as the fuel to produce it. Later he developed a saltworks using the fuel to boil seawater, and a glassworks.

A second period of industrial development occurred between 1848 and 1890. Five companies attempted to use the Blackstone. Unlike Sir William they had their works elsewhere—Weymouth in the first case, but Wareham in the others. One concern managed a contract to light Paris by Kimmeridge Oil-shale gas and for a short period in the late 1850s was also producing 50 tonnes of oil and 200 tonnes of fertiliser a month. The highlight of the period occurred during the next company's tenure when the works of the Wareham Oil and Candle Co succumbed to a common hazard and caught fire! A tonne of oil-shale was said to yield 34 litres of naphtha, 45 litres of oil, 51 kilogrammes of pitch and some paraffin wax and gas, but the 6·7 percent sulphur present ruined most ventures. 450m east of the Clavell Tower a clifftop trench marks the outcrop, but the only way to obtain specimens today is from the cliffs.

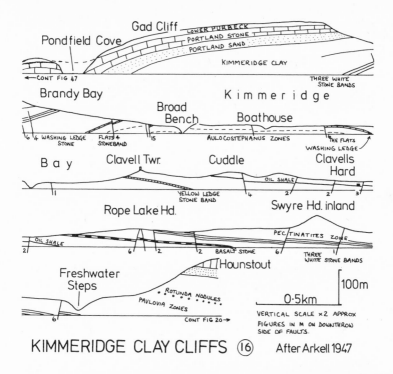

KIMMERIDGE CLAY CLIFFS ⑯ After Arkell 1947

The first distinctive headland east is Clavell's Hard. The ledge half-way down was probably quarried out. A tramway ran along it connecting the various oil-shale adit mouths. Several small faults are seen in the base of the headland which lies stratigraphically just above the middle of the Subplanites ammonite zones, 75m of shales and clays between the Yellow and White Stone Bands (Figure 16).

Ammonites are common only at certain levels in these zones but usually crushed. As usual they are identified by their ribbing and sutures—the distinctive furrow patterns made at the junction of the inner dividing walls or septa with the outer surfaces of the whorls. An additional feature, known as virgatotome ribbing, can be seen—the fine ribbing on the inner side of the whorls becomes coarse with irregular branching on the outer margin. Greater success is likely at Clavell's Hard if the shales are searched for various bivavles, *Lingula*, *Orbiculoidea* and *Protocardia*, and especially 3·5m of beds below the Blackstone, which contain radial plates of the free-swimming crinoid *Saccocoma*, usually preserved in bright pyrites.

Agile climbers can get up on to the ledge via the waterfall or near the adit on the south-east side. Other adits have already been closed by falling shale. This one probably survives because it is near the edge. It is a good guide to the Blackstone horizon and from it the bed can be traced east down to shore level. Figure 16 will guide the explorer walking east to Hounstout—beware of being trapped by the tide.

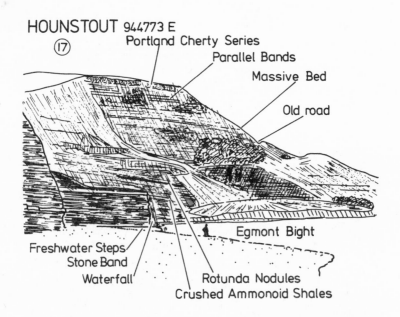

HOUNSTOUT 944773 E
(17)
Portland Cherty Series
Parallel Bands
Massive Bed
Old road
Egmont Bight
Freshwater Steps
Stone Band
Waterfall
Rotunda Nodules
Crushed Ammonoid Shales

HOUNSTOUT AND CHAPMAN'S POOL

From the car park at Chapman's Pool it is worth climbing to the summit of the Hounstout, 150m, which is bordered with buttresses and gullies in its Portland Stone capping. Below to the east, the Kimmeridge Clay is seen encircling Chapman's Pool, but at Emmits Hill it is hidden by screes. Emmits Hill provides the best section in the succeeding Portland Sands, visible between the scree and the vertical upper face where Portland Stone again caps the cliff. This well-exposed upper face, edge of the great plateau which forms the gentle southern limb of the Purbeck fold, continues to the right across Pier Bottom and on to St Alban's Head. Looking inland there is a distant view of Swanworth Quarry, a large modern working in the Portland Beds north of Worth Matravers (page 147). Notice how the valley forms reflect the geological succession.

The geology of Hounstout cliff (Figure 17) can be partly studied from landslips. Tracks lead over to Egmont Bight, thus enabling the student to resume the Kimmeridge Clay succession from close to the horizon of the Freshwater Steps Stone Band. The following details will be useful from Hounstout to St Alban's Head:

Portland Stone	{ Freestone Series, above	
	{ Cherty Series	18m
	Black sandstones; honeycombed	6·5m
	Three Parallel Bands; sandy prominent cement-	
	stones with shale partings, *Glaucolithites*	7m
Portland Sand	St Alban's Head Marls; light and dark grey	
	marls and shales, layers of *Exogyra nana*	13·5m
	White Cementstone; *Thracia depressa*,	
	Pleuromya tellina	0·7m
	Emmit Hill Marls; dark black sandy marls	8·5m
	Massive Bed; prominent sandstone	2m
	PAVLOVIA PALLASIOIDES & PAVLOVIA ROTUNDA ZONES	
	Hounstout Marl	15m
	Upper line of seepage visible after wet weather	
	on Hounstout	
	Hounstout Clay	6m
	Lower line of seepage visible after wet weather	
	on Hounstout	

	Rhynchonella and Lingula Beds	49m
	Rotunda Clays and Nodules	
Kimmeridge	Crushed Ammonoid Shales	33m
Clay	PECTINATITES PECTINATUS ZONE	
	Paravirgatites Clays and Shales	8m
	Pectinatites Clays with large nodules	5·5m
	Shales with hard band at top = the top of the	
	Freshwater Steps waterfall	6·5m
	Freshwater Steps Stone Band (top one of the	
	Three White Stone Bands)	
	Rest of Kimmeridge Clay sequence below,	
	see Figure 16.	

The lower part of the Crushed Ammonoid Shales can be examined along the east side of Egmont Bight. The ammonite *Pavlovia* occurs, though preservation is poor, as the name of the beds implies. Higher beds in the cliff can be identified by three means. The first prominent rib is a hard shale at the top of the Crushed Ammonoid Beds and above that are the two useful lines of seepage. Fallen blocks from the higher beds can be examined on the top of the landslip and the Massive Bed at the base of the Portland Sands reached without difficulty.

Entering Chapman's Pool, the dip brings the Crushed Ammonoid Shales to the cliff base and by the time the waterfall is reached their topmost hard shale is at beach level, forming the ledge around the east side of the Pool as far as the old boathouse—an old lifeboat station 1866–80s.

Above the hard shale band the cliffs are in the Rotunda Clays and Nodules, the basal part of 49m of Rhynchonella and Lingula Beds. Lying immediately above the hard shale, the nodules are calcareous mudstones and contain the best-preserved ammonites. The Lingula Beds follow, mainly shales, while the Rhynchonella Beds are marls again. Full of crushed ammonites, the latter form the rest of the cliffs and soon engage the attention of the least geologically minded visitor.

One of the main assets of Dorset is its superb coastal scenery and unspoilt walks. The greatest problem for the walker is which route to choose—the only answer is to walk every part in both directions, by cliff top and by beach.

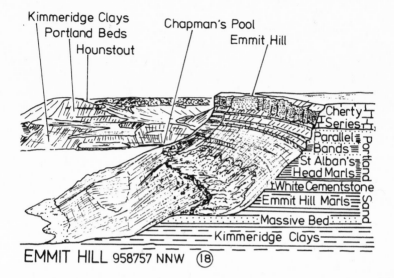

EMMIT HILL 958757 NNW ⑱

EMMIT HILL AND ST ALBAN'S HEAD

East of Chapman's Pool the path keeps to the base of the cliffs at first, actually on the scree-hidden higher Kimmeridge Clay succession. Blocks of fallen Portland material strew the slopes. The Portland Sand of the middle cliff face can be reached by climbing up the screes about 180m before Pier Bottom (Figure 18). The Three Parallel Bands are the most prominent feature and can be traced by eye as far as Hounstout.

Standing 106m above sea level, St Alban's Head is crowned by the tiny chapel of St Alban, its vaulted roof supported on a single pillar and originally surmounted by a fire basket lit as a beacon to warn ships. Shipwrecks were common below these wild and inaccessible cliffs. Standing anywhere between them and Durlston Head, it seems remarkable that the Portland Stone quarries, which here begin to honeycomb the cliffs, despatched their stone by sea. The St Alban's Head quarries were the highest of all and let their stone down the faces to the boats below. Evidently the craft were stout-bottomed, for the descent of the stone into the hold must have been hazardous in the smallest swell.

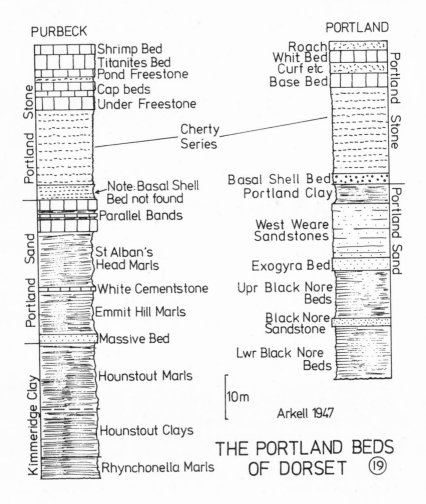

PURBECK

Shrimp Bed
Titanites Bed
Pond Freestone
Cap beds
Under Freestone

Portland Stone

Cherty
Series

Note: Basal Shell
Bed not found

Parallel Bands

Portland Sand

St Alban's
Head Marls

White Cementstone

Emmit Hill Marls

Massive Bed

Hounstout Marls

Kimmeridge Clay

Hounstout Clays

Rhynchonella Marls

PORTLAND

Roach
Whit Bed
Curf etc
Base Bed

Portland Stone

Basal Shell Bed
Portland Clay

West Weare
Sandstones

Exogyra Bed

Upr Black Nore
Beds

Black Nore
Sandstone

Lwr Black Nore
Beds

Portland Sand

10 m

Arkell 1947

THE PORTLAND BEDS
OF DORSET ⑲

Arriving at the edge of the headland, the geologist has an opportunity to memorise the Portland succession of Purbeck for comparison with that of Portland itself (Figure 19). The beds here are much thicker and they continue to thicken eastwards. For example, the Pond Freestone which was the upper of the two beds sought by the Purbeck quarrymen is 2m thick at St Alban's but increases to 3·5m at Seacombe. The Under Freestone, so thin as to be uneconomic at St Alban's, becomes 1m thick at Winspit, 2·5m at Seacombe and was the main bed sought in all the cliff face galleries.

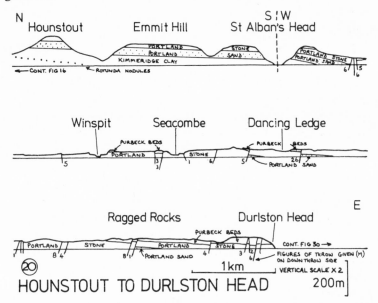

HOUNSTOUT TO DURLSTON HEAD

Below the coastguard station is a quarried ledge with a notable mushroom-shaped pillar left by the workmen. The stalk of the 'mushroom' is in the Pond Freestone for which the area was worked, and the head belongs to the Titanites Bed, the principal bed yielding specimens of the giant ammonite *Titanites*. The section can be continued on the inner face where 3m of Titanites Bed is followed by 3·5m of Shrimp Bed—so named because it yields remains of a primitive crustacean called *Callianassa* (Figure 21). Below the quarry edge the Cherty Series can be reached by steep paths down the screes. The Puffin Ledge is the most prominent datum there, a soft almost chert-less bed forming an eroded ledge on which the birds used to nest. The Portland Sands and Kimmeridge clays below are hidden by screes of waste, equivalents of the weares of Portland.

THE PORTLAND BEDS OF PURBECK

From St Alban's Head past Winspit, Seacombe and Dancing Ledge to Tilly Whim, the cliffs are riddled with quarry galleries. A good itinerary is to bus from Swanage to Worth Matravers and walk back along the coast.

The valley south from Worth Matravers passes through the finest limestone scenery in Purbeck, its hillsides terraced by lynchets of a medieval strip-farming system. Eventually the track arrives at the cliff face quarries, whose floor marks the top of the Cherty Series. The numerous galleries which lead off this level are driven into the Under Freestone, a fine cream-coloured oolitic limestone which has been worked out in huge chambers together with the Under Picking Cap above it. The latter was cut to waste simply to get at the freestone. A freestone is one which can be squared up in any direction, ie is independent of joints, grain or bedding planes.

The roof of each gallery is formed by the hard grey House Cap, 2·5m thick (Figure 22). Although giant ammonites *Titanites* can be found embedded in the base of the House Cap in places, the bed known as the Titanites Bed is 3·5m higher again. It forms the roof of the single higher gallery on the west side at Winspit, a gallery driven on the Pond Freestone, previously seen at St Alban's Head.

Below the quarry floor parts of the Cherty Series can be inspected when the sea is calm. The Puffin Ledge is 7m down, and beds around and below it have occasionally produced large ammonites. Uncertainty exists as to whether these are *Behemoth*, as they have been called, or forms of *Titanites*. They are certainly more inflated. Smaller forms found here, known as *Kerberites*, are also suggested to be the detached inner whorls of *Titanites*.

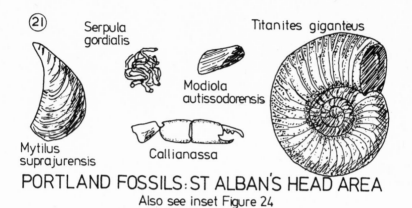

PORTLAND FOSSILS: ST ALBAN'S HEAD AREA
Also see inset Figure 24

WINSPIT GALLERIES 976761 NW ㉒

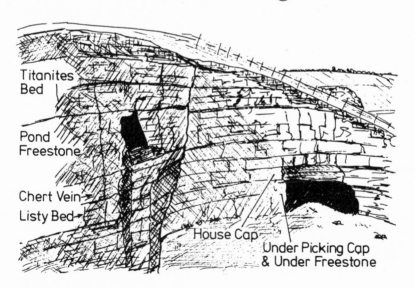

At Winspit the Kimmeridge Clay and Portland Sand have dipped below sea level and for 7km eastwards the cliffs are in Portland Stone. The beds dip gently seawards everywhere and undulate slightly along the cliffs. The latter feature is partly due to faulting, which here and there just brings the Portland Sand back up to sea level, allowing undermining and collapse of the Cherty and Stone Series. The largest fault on the coast occurs a short distance east of Dancing Ledge, allowing the sea to undermine until the east dip again brings the Portland Stone down to the level where it can protect itself.

Notice the general form of the cliffs and slopes along this coast. The vertical faces are almost wholly in Portland Stone Beds with Purbeck Beds making the bulk of the receding slopes above. The last galleries in the Portland Stone are the old workings known as Tilly Whim Cave which can be entered from the coast path. Above their western entrance there is a remarkable lens-shaped oyster bed, a local development at the level of the Titanites Bed. Fallen blocks of it clutter the central area of the quarry floor. Their weathered faces testify to the reason for discarding the bed. The Tilly Whim quarries were last worked in 1812.

Return to the Isle of Portland to compare the exposures there with those just examined. Those wishing to examine the Isle of Purbeck as a unit can continue north of Durlston Head with the famous Purbeck Beds type section (Chapter 7). It is one of the confusions of Dorset's prolific geology that both Portland and Purbeck Beds occur on both the Isles of Portland and Purbeck!

CHAPTER 6

The Isle of Portland

The present-day view of Portland from Wyke Regis gives little hint of its famous quarries, long isolation or peculiar history. The long triangular island is easily approached over the bridge at Small Mouth, yet before 1839 this was the site of a dangerous ferry passage, the only alternative to a walk the length of Chesil Beach! As the end of the beach is reached at Chesilton, the true scale and grandeur of the north end of the Isle becomes apparent, the Portland Stone Beds capping settled slopes of Portland Sands and Kimmeridge Clay.

The rock succession of Portland is:

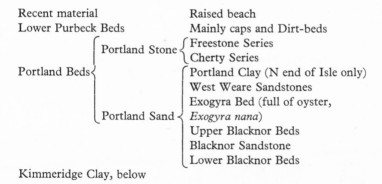

Recent material   Raised beach
Lower Purbeck Beds   Mainly caps and Dirt-beds

Portland Beds

Portland Stone — Freestone Series / Cherty Series

Portland Sand — Portland Clay (N end of Isle only) / West Weare Sandstones / Exogyra Bed (full of oyster, *Exogyra nana*) / Upper Blacknor Beds / Blacknor Sandstone / Lower Blacknor Beds

Kimmeridge Clay, below

The Kimmeridge Clay underlies the whole Isle but only out-crops at the northern end, where it extends around the lower slopes from Blacknor Battery on the west to Church Ope Cove on the east. The famous Kimmeridge 'Coal' oil-shale used to be visible between tide levels at Castletown. Nowadays the only Kimmeridge exposure occurs beneath natural landslips on the west coast at Tar Rocks. It is fortunate that the clays are built over or covered in stone waste everywhere, since this prevents their erosion and possible undermining of other beds. There is ample evidence of the weakness of the Kimmeridge Clay in historical records of the Isle, however—eg in 1698 during stone shipment for rebuilding St Paul's Cathedral the pier and way in Castletown were 'ruined by the sliding of the ground into the sea'. The sea still had easy access to the weak clay slopes until the construction of the breakwater, 1849–72.

WEST WEARE CLIFFS

Use Geological map No 324 and the 1:25000 SY67/77 to study Portland. On reaching the island, turn right after the roundabout and park in Victoria Square, to walk along the West Weares. Weares are the quarrymen's name for waste tips, here inextricably mixed up with natural landslips. The geology of the cliffs is shown in Figure 23.

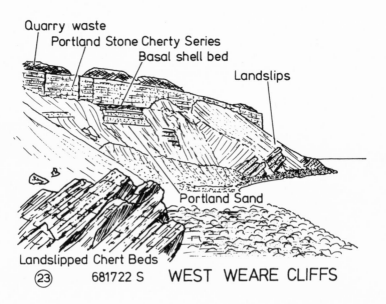

WEST WEARE CLIFFS

In addition to material from the upper faces, the fallen blocks also contain Lower Purbeck Beds, stripped off the highest levels of the Isle when quarrying began. Tipping over the cliffs was essential since the valuable stone lay about 18m below the surface. Tipping continued until sufficient ground had become involved for the quarries to use their old workings as dumps. So the weares now bring a variety of material within reach of geologists— blocks from Cherty and Freestone Series, Purbeck Beds, roach etc—and a wide range of fossils.

The western bastions of the Isle, at the top of the slope, are in the Portland Stone Cherty Series. Lines of black cherts are readily recognised in fallen blocks. With care it is possible to climb right up the screes to the base of these bluffs and examine the undercut beneath them, which marks the top of the less resistant Portland Sands and yields large ammonites. Impressions of many of these can be seen in the underside of the Cherty Series.

The Cherty Series begins with the famous Basal Shell Bed, 2m of hard crystalline limestone full of shells. This is the best Portland Bed of all for variety of fossils but, although well preserved, they are notoriously difficult to extract. Mainly lamellibranchs, they are illustrated in Figure 24. If the ascent proves impossible there are plenty of blocks on the natural landslips. Erosion of the Portland Sands and undermining of the Cherty Series is the cause of these falls, both Cherty and Freestone Series being cut by two large joint systems which allow the blocks to fall away. The joint systems are the only notable result of the involvement of the beds in the Weymouth anticline. They average 18m apart, trend NNE-SSW and east-west and leave the Portland Stone in large undamaged blocks, eminently suitable for quarry purposes (Figure 77).

In addition to Basal Shell Bed material, look for internal casts of *Trigonia incurva* and *Protocardia dissimilis* (Figure 24), which are common in some of the higher levels of the Cherty Series, and for fragments of fossilised trees in waste from the Lower Purbeck Dirt Beds. The Purbeck material is thinner bedded and varied, making the finer waste of the Weares. There is also less of it since natural erosion had removed these beds from the areas from which these West Weares are derived, Figure 77.

A third interest in the screes are the blocks of spongy-looking open-textured roach from the top of the Freestone Series. This stone, whose name means coarse quality, was unsuitable for fine architectural work, though it has been slabbed for cladding buildings as a special effect in modern times and was formerly used for rough construction, eg the Nothe fort at Weymouth. The cavities in roach are formed by the solution of shells buried in it. Two species dominate the rock: Portland 'screws' and 'Osses 'eads'. The former is the turreted gastropod *Aptyxiella portlandica*, which looks exactly like a corkscrew since the solution of the shell has usually left a perfect cast of its interior (Figure 24). 'Osses 'eads' was the quarrymen's name for *Laevitrigonia gibbosa*— again commonly dissolved, leaving external mould and internal cast within it (Figure 24). Both can prove difficult to extract—too

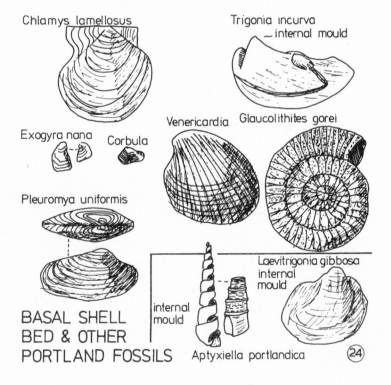

Chlamys lamellosus

Trigonia incurva
internal mould

Exogyra nana   Corbula

Venericardia   Glaucolithites gorei

Pleuromya uniformis

Laevitrigonia gibbosa
internal mould

BASAL SHELL
BED & OTHER
PORTLAND FOSSILS

internal mould

Aptyxiella portlandica   (24)

heavy hammering near them shatters the casts before they can be lifted out—but an hour or two spent on the scree waste is bound to be rewarding.

About halfway along the West Weares a large natural slip begins, affecting the Portland Beds as far south as Blacknor Battery. The cause is the underlying Kimmeridge Clay which can be located under the boulder-strewn shore at Tar Rocks. A slump cliff of Portland Sands, Blacknor Beds and sandstone is seen behind the beach.

A major interest of the Cherty Series is the consistent size and regular spacing of the chert nodules at any level in the beds. The regularity suggests that the silica material of which they are formed was part of the original sediment. The difficulty is to decide whether it formed the cherts at the same time as the surrounding limestones, or whether it remained in some soluble form until a later period. If the latter was so, why did the chert show preference for certain limestone courses only? Was it because of some slight difference in their composition? None has been detected which would explain this; however, in the Isle of Purbeck there are certainly cherts of secondary origin.

Returning to Chesilton, make for the top level above Fortuneswell, keeping left after the hairpin bend to reach the car park and vantage point (Figure 25). Here, even in clear weather, it is difficult to make out the far end of Chesil Beach some 16km away (Chapter 16). Immediately below the viewpoint was the track of the Merchants' Railway (Chapter 17). It can be traced around the head of the valley to the east and along the slopes of The Verne (built 1869 as a fortress, now Portland Prison).

From The Verne the Portland Stone Beds dip gently 1–2° south, soon becoming capped with Lower Purbeck Beds. The dip brings them down to 10m above sea-level at Portland Bill. These rocks form the last remnant of the south limb of the eroded and breached Weymouth anticline. Looking north over Chesil and Weymouth, imagine the beds on which you stand continuing up over those districts and uniting with their more folded and disturbed northern limb outcrop between Portesham and Osmington. Had these eroded beds been at sea level instead of the weaker

Portland Sands and Kimmeridge Clays which lie below them, then Portland might never have become an island. As it was, the breach was easily made through Portland Roads and only the late creation of Chesil Beach has maintained a modern physical link with the mainland.

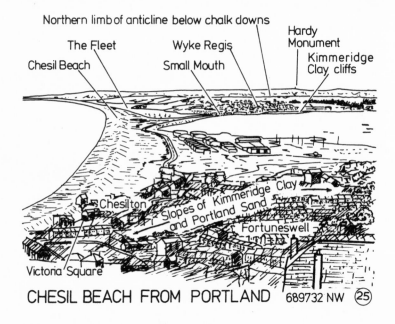

CHESIL BEACH FROM PORTLAND   689732 NW ㉕

The road towards Weston passes between Trade and Inmosthay quarries, both full of discarded waste but with a few outcrops in situ. A footpath from pre-quarrying days is still a right of way across Trade Quarries. Tramways and tunnels can be seen and the debris searched for casts of *Laevitrigonia* and *Aptyxiella*. Beyond the quarries St George's Church, built 1754–65 to replace the old church of St Andrew, falling into the sea at Church Ope Cove, is a fair copy of Wren's style by Thomas Gilbert.

THE FOSSIL GARDEN

On the main Easton road, stop at the office of Vickers Shipbuilding (Design), formerly that of Dorset Limestones. Behind it is the Fossil Garden, now neglected and far inferior to local private fossil gardens. A collection of specimens found in the quarries, these enormous finds are mainly giant ammonites, *Titanites*, up to 1m across, from the Whit Bed of the Freestone Series and many fragments of tufa-covered tree trunks (*Araucarites*, a conifer) from the Great Dirt Bed of the Lower Purbeck. The latter is a fossil soil formed during deltaic conditions following deposition of the Portland Freestone. Growing in these soils the forests were submerged in lagoons of calcium-carbonate-rich water which sheathed them in tufa. One example in the garden is a stump 3m high. Generally the interiors of the trees have been silicified, preserving their structural details in chalcedony. Dirt Beds can still be seen in the quarry faces and are described below (Freshwater Bay).

The future of the Fossil Garden seems uncertain. Unfortunately there is little room for it at the Portland Museum, 1·6km south, which also has large ammonite and tree fragments, and the boles of tree ferns (cycads—known locally as 'bird's nests') and masses containing these or other tree fragments as burrs.

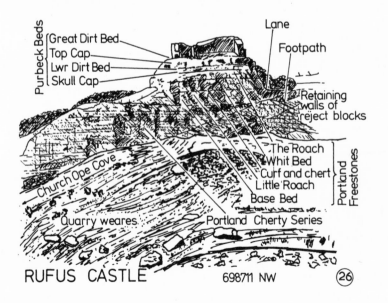

RUFUS CASTLE

Walk down the lane by the museum to reach Rufus Castle and Church Ope Cove. Existence of the castle has ensured the survival of the knoll on which it stands and of a continuous section up through Cherty and Freestone Series to Lower Purbeck. Unfortunately the Basal Shell Bed at the bottom is obscured by scree.

Leave the steps about half-way down and walk out on to the weares. The view of Rufus Castle (Figure 26), shows that the Freestone Series is 7·5m thick here. The castle walls stand on the level of the Top or Great Dirt Bed. Another full section through these beds is described at Holworth House (page 114).

The view south over Church Ope Cove reveals Southwell landslip, the last feature along this coast to be foundered by the underlying Kimmeridge Clay which then passes below shore level. Before returning up the lane a short walk leads north to a small modern quarry working Freestones along the previously sterilised zone of the old Portland railway line. Back at the museum, walk south-west to Perryfield Quarry which continues the Rufus Castle section farther up into the Lower Purbeck Beds (Figure 27).

PERRYFIELD QUARRY 694710 N ㉗

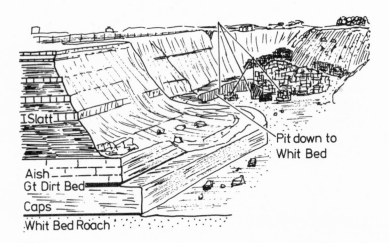

FRESHWATER BAY

Following the road towards Southwell take the coastal footpath at 690702 for Freshwater Bay. The path can be continued as far as Portland Bill, providing a continuous sequence of quarries and unfoundered sections in the Portland and Lower Purbeck Beds. About 180m along is a working quarry exposing the Freestones and Lower Purbecks, including both Lower and Great Dirt Beds. The entry level is at the base of the Freestones and the unworked part of these forms the lower face. Above them is a broad shelf from which the Purbeck beds have been stripped away (Figure 28). In waste north of the entrance there are cavity-riddled blocks from solution-widened joints with excellent samples of botryoidal calcite deposition, partly encrusted with small crystals of the same material. Undulating over old waste tips the path continues south at the level of the Cherty/Freestone Series junction.

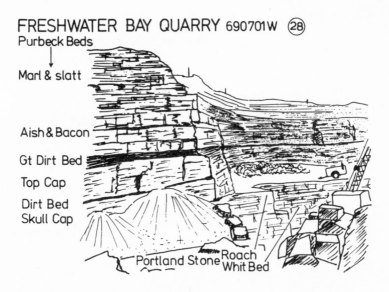

FRESHWATER BAY QUARRY 690701W ㉘
Purbeck Beds
Marl & slatt
Aish & Bacon
Gt Dirt Bed
Top Cap
Dirt Bed
Skull Cap
Portland Stone
Roach
Whit Bed

PORTLAND BILL

Many people find Portland a strange, almost depressing place. No doubt the scars of quarrying are responsible. Portland Bill has

lost much of its natural appearance due to the amount of wire
fencing there, but nevertheless it is still exhilarating. The sight of
the turmoil of currents in the off-shore race, the ever-present
winds and waves, and the fact that land is only seen in 60° of the
full 360°, all combine in its appeal. There are three geological
features to study.

On the east side of the Bill, working along the top of small
Freestone quarries, mound-like masses of a calcareous algae
Solenopora can be found. The Pulpit Rock, a natural sea-stack is
the second feature, and along the west shore there are good sections
of a raised beach, the limestone shelf on which it is based, the
beach deposit and the layer of sand and earth which caps it. The
exposure can be reached despite the fences and pebbles from local
outcrops seen in it, mixed with granite, porphyry and quartzites
which must have drifted east from the Budleigh Salterton Pebble
Beds or been brought into Lyme Bay from Dartmoor by the River
Teign.

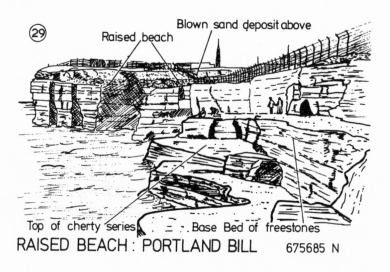

RAISED BEACH : PORTLAND BILL   675685 N

Formed when sea-level was temporarily higher than it is now,
at the close of the Ice Age, the raised beach is of Eemian interglacial age. It indicates colder waters than today's, for many of the
mollusc shells in it belong to species which now live along the shores

of northern England and Scotland.

The exposures of Lower Purbeck at Portland will have whetted the student's appetite for the next part of the Jurassic historical sequence—for which he must go again to Purbeck, to Durlston Bay.

CHAPTER 7

Isle of Purbeck: East Coast

On the Durlston Head to Studland Bay coast the beds all dip northwards as part of the basic anticlinal structure of Purbeck (Chapter 12 and Figure 30). The underlying Kimmeridge Clay and Portland Sand, seen previously in west Purbeck, have dipped below sea-level here due to the easterly plunge of the anticline. Swanage is the ideal centre to study all the formations, and also to compare their coastal outcrops with their behaviour as they strike west through the Isle.

THE PURBECK BEDS TYPE SECTION

Pride of place locally must be taken by the sections of Durlston Bay, the type area for the Purbeck Beds of Jurassic time throughout the world, formed when the shoreline mainly lay to the east and

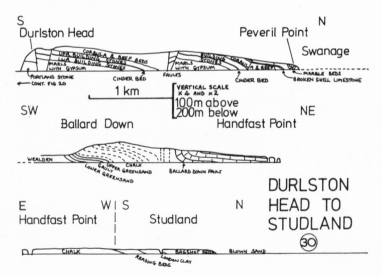

extensive fresh-water and brackish lakes and swamps covered this part of Dorset. Interruptions occurred with submergences and deposition of marine beds. There is a similarity between the Purbeck Beds and those of the Rhaetic—Jurassic times opened and closed with a mixture of marine and freshwater conditions (Chapter 1).

To follow the succession in order, travel south from Swanage to Durlston Head. With its holm oak, tamarisk trees and curios of the stone trade, the headland is popular with tourists. The area is now part of the Dorset Heritage Coast. There is a Stone Trail with leaflets to guide the visitor. Largest curiosity is Durlston Castle, whose original owner, George Burt, decorated it with stone tablets recording various texts and geographical facts. His biggest memento of the stone trade is the Great Globe, standing in a garden on the south-east. Weighing 40 tonnes, it was carved in sections at John Mowlem's works in Greenwich (Chapter 17). Burt and Mowlem glorified Swanage in the last century, as the town's role changed from stone to tourism (Figure 80).

ORIGIN OF THE BROKEN BEDS

The Broken Beds are one of the most intriguing features of the Purbeck succession. Undoubtedly the most important cause of shattering was the folding of the region. Even the largest blocks are made of thinly bedded material, rocks which could not stand much pressure and were trapped between the more resistant and competent beds of Portland Stone below and the Purbeck Building Stones above. These could absorb the forces more readily, but the Broken Beds were incompetent and shattered.

Another factor is the similarity of Purbeck times to those of the Rhaetic. In both the marine invasions produced highly saline environments at times, with evaporation of shallow areas of sea-water leading to the formation of gypsum and anhydrite. Locally gypsum is found higher up the succession. Further east it is present in quantity at the base of the Purbeck Beds (Portsdown borehole, near Portsmouth). Evidence suggests that gypsum was also present in large amounts in the lowest Purbeck Beds of Dorset and was later removed by solution. This could have helped the collapse of the Broken Beds during later folding. So the Broken Beds are mainly due to tectonic shattering, but their destruction was aided by the solution and removal of quantities of evaporite minerals originally present in them. One unfortunate feature of Durlston Bay is the poor exposure of the Dirt Beds and their tufa-covered tree stumps at the south end of the bay. However, the Broken Beds are well seen there amid fallen material.

The table below shows the succession. Although little can be seen in position in the south part of the bay, there is plenty to search for. After the Broken Beds come the Marls with Gypsum, mainly pale grey shales and clays with the gypsum concentrated in 3·5–7m of beds, 7–12m above the base. The shaley material should be examined carefully since these beds yield insect remains —beetles, cockroaches, grass-hoppers, dragonflies and daddy-longlegs among them. The remains are mainly wings and wing-cases (elytra), detached and not in particular layers. The most remarkable feature is their preservation; the cases retain their colour and the wings their delicate detail. These insects are of no use for stratigraphical zoning, however; there are just not enough of them, although they were forms of life which moved freely from place to place (see ostracods, below).

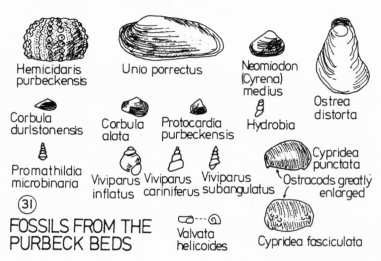

Hemicidaris
purbeckensis

Unio porrectus

Neomiodon
(Cyrena)
medius

Ostrea
distorta

Corbula
durlstonensis

Corbula
alata

Protocardia
purbeckensis

Hydrobia

Promathildia
microbinaria

Viviparus
inflatus

Viviparus
cariniferus

Viviparus
subangulatus

Cypridea
punctata
Ostracods greatly
enlarged

(31)

FOSSILS FROM THE
PURBECK BEDS

Valvata
helicoides

Cypridea fasciculata

Figure 31 shows some of the more likely fossil finds. Note the absence of ammonites, excluded from the area with the ending of deeper water conditions at the close of the Portlandian stage and not to return until fully marine conditions re-appeared with deposition of the Lower Greensand (page 93).

The Purbeck Beds succession:

			Alternative ideas of Dr R. Casey, see below
3·4m (+?)	Viviparus Clays		
14m	Marble Beds and Ostracod Shales	Upper Purbeck Beds (Jurassic)	Durlston Beds (Cretaceous)
1·5m	Unio Beds		
3m	Broken Shell Limestone		
9m	Chief Beef Beds		
10·3m	Corbula Beds		Suggested Jurassic/
15·2m	Upper Building Stones	Middle Purbeck Beds (Jurassic)	←Cretaceous boundary
2·5m	Cinder Bed		
1·4m	Lower Building Stones		
0·3m	Mammal Bed		
41m	Marls with Gypsum	Lower Purbeck Beds (Jurassic)	Lulworth Beds (Jurassic)
4·6m	Broken Beds and Cypris Freestones		
5·8m	Caps and Dirt Beds		

Just south of the Zig Zag Path, the dip brings the Building Stones down to beach level. The Cinder Bed is one of the most distinctive in the succession. A dense mass of the oyster *Ostrea distorta*, it earns its name from the clinker-like appearance of its weathered outcrops. The bed marks a widespread and important marine inundation, and occurs everywhere in the Purbeck succession at this horizon. The bed has been suggested as the boundary between the Jurassic and Cretaceous systems, on the grounds that it is a readily recognisable horizon corresponding to beds in Lincolnshire which mark a definite advance of marine conditions. However, since brackish and deltaic conditions returned to dominate the rest of the Purbeck deposition, this would put the boundary in the middle of a formation whose two parts were very similar. A point in favour of the idea is that it would get rid of the more thorny problem at the top of the Purbeck Beds where the division from an equally deltaic Wealden has always been difficult to fix. If the idea is accepted it will mean the adoption of Lulworth Beds as the name for the Jurassic part of the Purbeck formation and Durlston Beds for the Cretaceous part.

Look for a thin bed of crushed *Protocardia* (Figure 31) in the middle of the Cinder Bed. The echinoid or sea-urchin *Hemicidaris purbeckensis*, and *Laevitrigonia gibbosa* have also been discovered, but the student will be lucky indeed to locate one. Both indicate a brief marine habitat for the first time since the Portland Beds. However, absence of ammonites, crinoids, etc, shows the conditions were not fully marine.

The jumbled cliff at the Zig Zag Path is due to a landslip in 1960, but there is also a double fault at the northern side. The Cinder Bed is a guide to the movements (Figure 32). The succession seen so far is repeated again in the northern part of the bay, the faults leaving the geologist to begin again in the Marls with Gypsum.

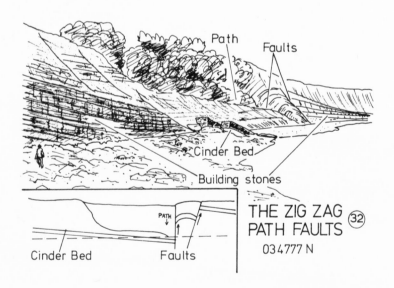

THE ZIG ZAG PATH FAULTS (32)
034777 N

THE MAMMAL BED

In 1856 in a specially dug cliff-top pit north of these faults, S. H. Beckles made exciting finds of mammal remains. Prolonged subsequent searches have never yielded so many as Beckles found in what was an exceptionally rich pocket, though some have turned up at the base of the Lower Building Stones on the foreshore of the southern section just described. To vertebrate palaeontologists the Mammal Bed is the most important bed of the Jurassic system. Nineteen species were found, all of cat or rat size, mainly tree-dwelling vegetarians though the larger were carnivorous.

The Mammal Bed is essentially a Dirt Bed or fossil soil, the remains of muddy banks covered with swamp vegetation. Reptiles are also found in it and at other horizons locally—eg crocodiles, many of them dwarf size, only 45cm long when fully grown. Dinosaurs such as *Echinodon* and *Iguanodon* also occur and turtle plates and bones (Figure 62).

The Lower and Upper Building Stones are obviously named because of their importance to the quarrying trade. Only parts of their sequence are usable and old quarrying areas soon confirm that much is cut to waste. Examine the Lower Building Stones where they descend to beach level for the second time, north of the double fault. The Mammal Bed at the base and the Cinder Bed on top are readily identifiable markers, but there are two other notable beds to be located. 5m below the Cinder Bed is 1m of Cherty Freshwater Limestone, full of perfectly preserved freshwater snails, gastropods, including *Valvata*, *Hydrobia* and *Planorbis* species (Figure 31). Difficult to extract, they can be seen in limestone and cherty material. The Purbeck Marble Beds, seen later, are also full of freshwater snails. Note that some Purbeck chert nodules are full of sponge spicules, *Spongilla purbeckensis*. Also study a noticeable black shale, 25cm thick, which lies 1·2m below the Cherty Freshwater Limestone or 3m above the Mammal Bed, and contains insect and fish remains.

PURBECK FISH AND OSTRACODS

Fossil fish occur in the Lower and Upper Building Stones. Unlike the primitive, heavily armoured Upper Palaeozoic fish, these had more complex and efficient skeletons, jaws and scales. Few Cretaceous fish derive from them, however, and Purbeck fish seem to represent a peak development of older forms. At least twenty-four species have been found, the majority being ganoids, fish about 30cm in length, fairly deep-bodied in life and covered with heavy enamelled rhombic scales. Discovery of these specimens obviously depends on being able to expose a fairly large area of rock, an unsafe process along these cliffs.

One group of fossils, the ostracods, is abundant everywhere in the Purbeck succession. Ostracods are little bivalved crustaceans (water-fleas), the best zone fossils in the Purbeck Beds. They swarmed in the Purbeck shallows, with species adapted to fresh, marine or brackish water, and so they occur widely throughout the Purbeck sediments. Fortunately the abundance of various species changes vertically—and this makes them useful zone fossils. There is no problem in collecting a large number. They appear as blackish spots on shaly samples and in some limestones form the bulk of the bed, but the difficulty is their small size—up to 1mm across. They must be identified under a microscope.

The repetition of beds continues and soon the Cinder Bed reaches shore level again, followed by the Upper Building Stones. Whereas the Lower Building Stones are varied and predominantly freshwater deposits, the Upper Building Stones are more uniform in character and mainly marine—pale, thin, shelly limestones. Their shale partings contain the ostracod *Cypridea punctata*. Fish and reptilian remains are again important. Assemblages of *Pecten, Ostrea, Corbula* and *Protocardia* mark marine phases throughout the Building Stones, while the freshwater beds contain *Viviparus, Hydrobia, Valvata* etc (Figure 31).

The succession becomes more variable again in the shales, marls and limestones of the Corbula Beds which follow. Marine shells denote their chief source with, as the name implies, several species of *Corbula, Pecten* and *Protocardia* abundant in fallen blocks and the ostracod *Cypridea punctata* again plentiful. The Corbula Beds also contain 'Beef', the fibrous calcite previously studied near Lyme Regis (Chapter 2), and the crystalline form of gypsum, selenite (page 51). The crystals here are often flattened and elongated, growing in partings in the shaley beds.

Beef deposits increase to such an extent that the next 9m of the Purbeck succession are known as the Chief Beef Beds, fibrous calcite layers and shales between thin shaley limestones. Once fallen to the shore the beef soon disintegrates. The top of these beds is easy to locate, a 3·5m limestone bed, the thickest development of limestone seen since leaving the Building Stones.

This is the Broken Shell Limestone, made mainly from fragments of *Cyrena*, *Unio* and *Viviparus*. At the first way up the cliff south-west of Peveril Point the Corbula Beds are at the base, the scramble up is over the Chief Beef Beds, and, although it is missing just there due to falls, the Broken Shell Limestone horizon is at the cliff top. Descending north to sea-level it becomes a key horizon to the fold structures at Peveril Point and helps to locate the Purbeck Marble exposures there.

PEVERIL POINT

Approaching the point, the cliff above the limestone is very degraded—thin, greenish beef and limestone beds, known as the Unio Beds. In addition to *Unio,* fish and turtle remains, and fossilised droppings, coprolites, also occur. One carbonaceous limestone is known as the Crocodile Bed.

At Peveril Point the beds are folded into a W-shape, the outer limbs of the figure being the Broken Shell Limestone. It forms the two prominent reefs, extending seaward of the point for nearly 1·5km. The Danish raiding fleet was supposed to have been wrecked on them in 877. The north and south dips into the W-formation are easily seen in the reefs, but the Broken Shell Limestone is no help in revealing the small central upfold since it does not rise to beach level in the middle of the 'W'. Like the Lulworth Crumple (page 126), and the Broken Beds, the Peveril Point folds are further evidence of incompetent behaviour in the

Broken Shell Limestone
Unio Beds
Marble Beds and ostracod
shales

(33)
PEVERIL POINT & THE MARBLE BEDS 042786 SW

Purbeck succession during the folding of the Isle. Figure 33 shows the outcrop of the Marble Beds south of the shelter. An alternative section occurs on the north side of the point, the northern limb of the W-fold. On the ledges leading back to Swanage, the last visible bed of the Purbeck succession is the Broken Shell Limestone, forming a ledge with peculiar surface hollows north of the Grosvenor Hotel.

SWANAGE BAY

Swanage promenade yields no evidence of the Purbeck–Wealden junction which lies close to the Swan Brook 0·5km north of the town centre. The junction is the local outcrop of the Jurassic/Cretaceous boundary which has long been placed at this change from fossiliferous Purbeck marls and limestones to relatively barren Wealden sands and marls. Dr R. Casey's ideas about the Cinder Bed, referred to above, would mean the local boundary being in Durlston Bay instead, and would transfer much of the Middle and all the Upper Purbeck Beds—including the Marble Beds of Peveril Point—into the Cretaceous system.

The first cliffs of Wealden Beds coincide with the point where the seafront road turns inland towards Ulwell. The road in fact follows the line of the Ulwell Fault which, downthrowing 1·5m on its west side passes north-west into the chalk ridge between Ballard Down and Godlingston Hill (Chapter 13).

Wealden times were freshwater in character (Chapter 1), the beds being deposited in deltas and lakes with no marine intervals. They are divided into two groups. The lower and thickest group— the clayey and sandy beds seen at Swanage—are known as the Wealden Variegated Marls and Sands. Only the last 10m of deposits at the north end of the bay belong to the second group— the Wealden Shales which are more important for fossil remains.

The cliffs at Swanage reveal the brilliant red, orange, yellow and purple colours of the Variegated Marls and Sands. Beds of coarse grey quartz grit are the thickest units. Here and there, there are lignite beds and hard ribs of dark brown ironstone. The shaley beds can be searched for ostracods. Since much of the material came from re-uplifted lands to the west there is a good deal of Devonian and Cornish type rock present—pebbles of Carboniferous (Culm) chert, pieces of tourmaline, slate, and especially the thick coarse quartz grits. It is fortunate that the Wealden Beds are well exposed three times on the coast for like so many of the county's formations they quickly grass over inland. At Swanage an opportunity to see them inland occurs at the brickworks north-west of the town.

PUNFIELD COVE

Punfield Cove is the name given to the north-west area of Swanage Bay, roughly at the intersection of grid lines 04/81. Access can be gained by a rough path which runs up through a large recess to the cliff-top route. The area is very overgrown and slipped but its significance lies in the ammonites found here, indicating a return to fully marine conditions for the first time since the deposition of the Portland Beds (Chapter 1).

This submergence of the Wealden landscape by the Lower Greensand seas, the Aptian transgression, is the first unconformity met with north of Swanage and marks the beginning of marine transgressions which continued throughout the Cretaceous period.

1. Deposition of Jurassic and Wealden.

2. Earth movements.
   Folding faulting and
   erosion of existing beds.

   Submergence.
   Aptian transgression and deposition of Lower Greensand.

3 Renewed submergence, Albian transgression, deposition
   of Gault, Upper Greensand and Chalk.

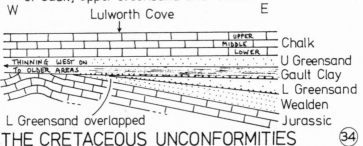

THE CRETACEOUS UNCONFORMITIES   (34)

The Lower Greensand sea occupied a large basin over The
Weald, Hampshire and Dorset, the earth movements which
allowed its invasion also folding older rocks in the Weymouth area
to the west. So, traced westward, the Dorset Lower Greensand
thins on to the folded areas, in some parts planing off the top of
the older rocks involved (Figure 34).

How the beds came to be named Greensands and divided into
Upper and Lower is one of those peculiar compound mistakes of
geological literature. William Smith used the term first for some
beds in Wiltshire and it was then applied in Kent. Eventually it
was realised that the Wiltshire beds lay above the Gault while
the Kent beds lay below it—so there had to be an Upper and
Lower Greensand with the Gault in between. In Punfield Cove
the student seems to see everything except the green colour,
which is due to the mineral glauconite, an indicator of a shallow
water marine origin. As glauconite weathers, its iron content
oxidises, giving the beds the red, yellow and brownish hues seen
in these cliffs (also Golden Cap etc, Chapter 3).

A famous bed in the succession is the 37cm Punfield Marine Band. It is full of fossil molluscs and is yet another geological misnomer! The river which had brought the Wealden Bed material from the West Country continued to supply sediment to the Lower Greensand seas, producing both the Dorset beds and the Atherfield Clay in the thick Lower Greensand deposits of the southern Isle of Wight.

Then a slight elevation of the land occurred, which had the effect of moving the river estuary farther east. Freshwater lamellibranchs were able to occupy the Lulworth area, while farther down the estuary, over what is now Swanage Bay, brackish conditions created the Punfield Marine Band. Still further east, in the Isle of Wight, accumulation of the Atherfield Clay was interrupted by a sandy development known as the Crackers. So, the Punfield *Marine* Band is the one bed in the Lower Greensand of the cove which indicates brackish water!

As shown in Figure 34 the Lower Greensand had been laid against lands to the west and thinned on to them. The thickness formed was altered by the tilting and erosion which followed, and the Gault and Upper Greensand was then laid on top. This also thinned westward on to what were still the adjacent land areas, but it differs from the Lower Greensand as it overlapped the former and spread much farther west again. The northern part of Punfield Cove contains between 50 and 60m of poorly exposed Gault and Upper Greensand.

The Gault beds are blackish clays. At the northern end of the cove large numbers of sandstone doggers can be seen in the slumped material, but barely 12m of Upper Greensand is exposed in situ. This is the top of the formation, the *dispar* zone, with sandstones and stone bands so rich in the oyster *Exogyra conica* that the top 2m is known as the Exogyra Sandstone. *Exogyra* and the spirally-coiled calcareous tubes secreted by worms, *Serpula concava*, are undoubtedly the two most common fossils throughout the Upper Greensand. In the 5·4m of beds below the Exogyra Sandstone, the ammonite *Mortoniceras* (formerly *Pervinquiera*) and the sea-urchin *Cardiaster fossarius* may be found.

BALLARD DOWN TO HANDFAST POINT

Exploration is difficult along the next part of the coast, where the great chalk ridge of the Purbeck Hills reaches the shoreline. Much of this area can only be seen by boat—a special hiring must be made or a trip booked on one of the larger forty-seat launches which run cruises to the headlands. These give the geologist a forty-minute trip and, with camera at the ready and the morning sun on the cliffs, some fine photographs can be taken, compensation for the fact that many of the chalk zones are poorly fossiliferous.

The Dorset chalk here is so shattered and crystalline through its involvement in the Purbeck fold that it is useless for the study of either fossils or stratigraphy. Fortunately the Lower Chalk (Cenomanian) beds are unaffected at most localities. They can be examined on shore at the northern end of Punfield Cove, together with Middle Chalk beds exposed at low tide in upturned ledges below Ballard Down.

The Cenomanian beds are partly obscured by the slumping in Punfield Cove and the fallen material includes boulders from higher chalk zones of course. A greenish chloritic marl can be identified at the base (see Durdle Cove, page 124) with ribbed rhynchonellid brachiopod shells. Hard, splintery chalk follows and the next distinctive feature is the bluish-tinged *plenus* Marl. Taking to the sea ledges, reach the two zones of the Middle Chalk —the *Inoceramus labiatus* and *Terebratulina lata* zones. They are hard and unfortunately not very fossiliferous; rather than risk scrambling the lower cliffs, it is best to try and relate the fallen boulders back on the beach to their correct zones in the chalk. The tip of Ballard Point is in the lowest Upper Chalk zone, *Holaster planus*. Both point and coast beyond can only be examined by boat.

THE BALLARD DOWN FAULT

Figure 30 shows the attitude of the beds in the cliff but attention is bound to be absorbed by the unique Ballard Down Fault, visible

319m north of the point—it has puzzled and intrigued geologists for years. The early geological survey of Purbeck was begun on this coast and the fault dominated the structural interpretation put on the whole Isle.

No doubt the fault is a major feature of the district and must run westward for some distance. As yet there is no evidence that it continues as far as the ridge behind Lulworth and Durdle Coves at the far end of the Isle, or similarly that a westerly course would be confined to the chalk of the Purbeck Hills. If the fault is present it may well pass out into the Tertiary sands and clays of the heathlands to the north. Clearly the Tertiary beds were also involved in the folding of Purbeck (as shown by their upended outcrop against the chalk at Creechbarrow, page 166) and the fault was contemporary with this folding.

There is much to be discovered about the Ballard Down Fault and no proof of its origin, only theories. The solutions put forward have been an unconformity, southward overthrust, northward overthrust or normal fault downthrown to the north and 'onion-scale' adjustment faulting.

If time permits, the relevant facts can be examined by heaving-to a short distance off the cliff. The beds below the fault are nearly vertical and cut off by the fault plane, but those above run parallel to it. Both are in the *mucronata* zone chalk. Notice, however, that the northerly dip of the beds beneath the fault decreases in the lower zones towards Ballard Point.

If sea conditions permit close examination of the cliff, observe the harder, more shattered condition of the chalk below the fault plane. It is cleaved by calcite veins and slickensides, most shear planes dipping 60–70° south. Both shears and bedding planes are bent back south a little as they approach the fault plane. At first this seems to suggest thrust movement was involved—either the chalk above the fault being pushed southwards, or that below being upturned and pushed northwards against the fault plane. A southerly thrust would surely have shattered the chalk above the fault, but it is only compacted softer material, much less sheared and altered. This first idea goes totally against the structural origin of Purbeck, which forms an asymmetrical anticline

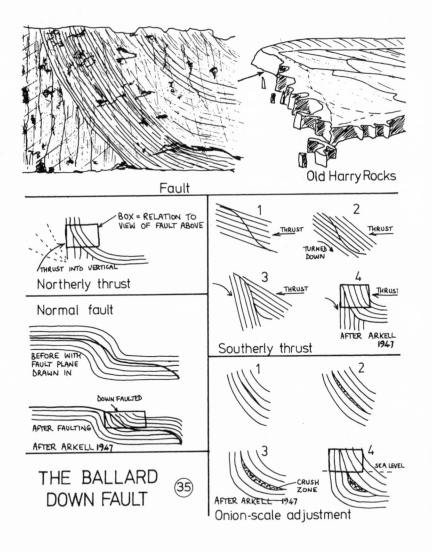

Old Harry Rocks

Fault

BOX = RELATION TO
VIEW OF FAULT ABOVE

THRUST INTO VERTICAL

Northerly thrust

Normal fault

BEFORE WITH
FAULT PLANE
DRAWN IN

DOWN FAULTED

AFTER FAULTING

AFTER ARKELL 1947

THE BALLARD
DOWN FAULT   35

1   THRUST   2   THRUST
TURNED
DOWN

3   THRUST   4   THRUST
AFTER ARKELL
1947

Southerly thrust

1   2

3   4   SEA LEVEL
CRUSH
ZONE
AFTER ARKELL 1947
Onion-scale adjustment

produced by *northward* movement.

Figure 35 illustrates a second thrust suggestion—that the Purbeck fold was at an early stage and continued northerly pressure then bent the fault plane itself upwards. The chalk beneath continued to push against it and was turned into a vertical attitude beneath the fault-plane. The problem with this theory is the difference between the chalk above and below the fault. How could the chalk below be so intensively sheared while the beds above were relatively unaffected?

With an unconformity clearly out of the question what alternatives are left to ponder on as the boat rocks gently below the cliff-face? A very low-angled normal fault is one, also illustrated in Figure 35. It would involve a great deal of lateral movement, but it could explain the slight southward bend at the top of the chalk beneath. The weight alone of downward moving beds above the fault could have produced this. The movement was probably a gravity slide caused by the severity of the folding.

The last theory illustrated is 'onion-scale' adjustment faulting. As the Purbeck fold increased in severity, the upper chalk beds would have been severely compressed in the foresyncline of the fold. To escape this pressure they are believed to have 'popped' out like the outer layers of a squeezed onion, while the lower beds could only yield by crushing in a zone now just below sea level at the Ballard Down Cliffs.

Two explanations have been offered for the fault's possible presence at the western end of Purbeck. The original geological survey, convinced that it was there, placed its outcrop parallel to the coast and just inland of the Durdle Cove-Bat's Head cliffs. The more recent memoir by Dr Arkell suggests that, if it is present, the crushed zone of the onion-scale idea has been lost by cliff erosion west of Bat's Head (page 119), in which case the present cliffs must be the beds above the fault plane.

What of the idea noted above that a westward combination of the fault may pass out into the Tertiary heathlands in places? Could the fault pass out of the Chalk on the south side of its outcrop instead of at the western end? A fault cuts obliquely across the neck of land between Man O'War and Durdle Coves, cutting out parts of the Purbeck and Wealden sequences there (page 144). Projected westwards its plane would pass close to Bat's Head, near the offshore reef of Portland Beds known as The Cow. This hypothesis would fit Arkell's suggested loss of the crushed zone by erosion.

During the winter season or in poor summer weather, the geologist must be content to follow the cliff-top path from Punfield to Handfast Point and see nothing of the Ballard Down Fault. The form of the down provides a clue to the bedding beneath, however, the high ground at the southern end being in the vertical or steeply dipping chalk below the fault-plane. Beyond the fault outcrop the down flattens and slopes gently northwards over the nearly horizontal *mucronata* chalk above the fault-plane. At Handfast Point numerous sea-stacks are cut in this fairly resistant material. The base of those stacks can be reached along the ledges from Studland at low tide, passing several more in partly detached stage. The *mucronata* zone chalk is at its most fossiliferous in the middle of its beds, and fallen blocks may be found on the small beaches around Handfast Point, where the largest stack is known as Old Harry.

In the south-west corner of Studland Bay the chalk dips below the Tertiary beds to form the great synclinal cradle of the Dorset heaths. Here is the third unconformity seen since leaving Swanage; the surface of the chalk is eroded and irregular, blackened flints from it being buried in the Tertiary beds above. The chronological sequence followed in preceding chapters is now continued with the Heathland Coasts. For those who have fallen under the spell of the Isle of Purbeck, Chapter 12 covers the inland districts and Chapter 17 the Purbeck stone trades.

CHAPTER 8

The Heathland Coasts

The Tertiary Beds of Dorset have very limited coastal exposures, due partly to their own character and partly because they are extensively built over in Bournemouth and Poole and the cliffs of these resorts are out of bounds to the public.

STUDLAND CLIFFS

Studland Cliffs expose the lowest beds of the heathland, resting on an eroded chalk surface. Make for the ravine leading off the lane at 038825 and follow it to the beach. The chalk surface is revealed at the south end. Heavily eroded by uplift and solution following its formation, the surface is covered by Reading Beds, their base full of blackened rolled flints derived from destruction of the chalk. There is also much dark brown ironstone. Returning north along the beach, the succession continues with clays and sands of the Reading Beds, red yellow and white in colour where exposed by slips. Undergrowth hides the junction with the London Clay. The next exposures are at the north end of the beach, the fantastically coloured Redend Sandstone, part of the Bagshot Beds. Intricate cross-bedding combined with the colours creates a wood-grain effect. The spot is a favourite one for carving initials. Look for the oldest dates—their age is surprising, the sands more durable than they appear.

Hardening on contact with the sea, the sands create the ledges of Redend Point. Here a number of ironstone-lined solution pipes penetrate the cliff, but they are not vertical, suggesting that they were formed before the beds were tilted by fold movement. Beyond the ledges, the top part of the Redend Sandstones consists of very different blackish clays filled with Eocene plant fragments, now the best local exposure of Tertiary flora. In the days when clay pits were hand dug layer by layer, beautiful plant specimens were commonly exposed. The section ends at Studland Beach, the Tertiary Beds disappearing beneath a cover of sand dunes.

The rest of the Tertiary succession in South Dorset is:

OLIGOCENE
    Creechbarrow Limestone and other beds. Marine
    becoming shallow with time. In Hants.   81m

EOCENE
    Barton Beds; including Hengistbury Beds and
    Highcliffe Sands. Shallow marine and estuarine.   20m

    Bracklesham Beds:
    Boscombe Sands; near shore deposits.   30m
    Bournemouth Marine Beds; seaward side of delta.   45–60m

    Bagshot Beds:
    Bournemouth Freshwater Series; deltaic.   121m
    ˙Agglestone Grit below, see page 165.

The friable nature of the Tertiary cliffs and the need to preserve beach and cliff amenities have combined to sterilise much of the Poole–Bournemouth cliffs. Sea walls foot all the faces, yet while these protect the cliffs from erosion they have denied the beach its sources of sand. Despite protective groynes, beach material has gradually drifted away and periodically must be topped up by sand dredged and pumped from offshore. For safety reasons the cliffs are now out of bounds, the only open part remaining being Canford Cliffs. Figure 36 shows the Tertiary plant beds which occur in the area in thin impure beds of pipeclay. These mainly sandy Bournemouth Freshwater Beds were deposited by the same Eocene river system originating from South-West England which formed the main Pipeclay Series of the heathlands. Their typically deltaic lenses of material also contain quartz-tourmaline or schorl rock, etc. Rapid variations from white to yellow sand, laminated carbonaceous clays and thin pipeclays can be observed.

BOURNEMOUTH CLIFFS ③⑥

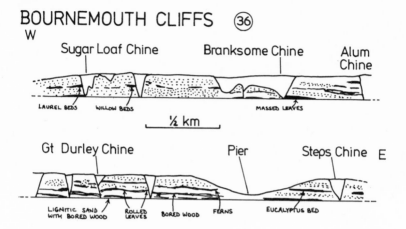

The darker clays contain pyrite material, sometimes in the form marcaiste. An old industry locally was the manufacture of copperas or hydrous ferrous sulphate from these materials. It was used in black dyeing. Old copperas houses existed in Alum and Boscombe Chines at one time. Ferrous sulphate also occurs native in the local cliffs as the yellowish green mineral melanterite—see Hengistbury Head, below. Alum Chine's name commemorates another dyer's product formerly obtained from these clay beds—hydrated potassium sulphate, obtained by roasting the material and then immersing it in solutions which dissolved out the chemical. It was used as a fixative in dyes.

HENGISTBURY HEAD

It is best to make a circuit of the headland, working first along the shore. The base is in Boscombe Sands, a layer of flint pebbles at their top marking the junction with the dingy green Hengistbury Beds. Although the latter are marine, land was evidently nearby at the time for their dull colour is due to carbonaceous material from drifted plant debris washed into the sea by rivers. The Upper Hengistbury Beds (Figure 37) contain up to five layers of prominent ironstone doggers. Some of the doggers contain embedded plant stems as well as sharks' teeth confirming the marine origin of the beds. Higher up the cliffs a change of colour to white and cream marks the Highcliffe Sands and, finally, at the top there are Pleistocene gravels from which Mesolithic flints and Iron Age pottery have been recovered.

Along the whole cliff-face the most unusual feature is the yellow discolouration everywhere. This is the melanterite (copperas) mineral. It forms brittle crusts difficult to sample on the clayey faces but more easily preserved as stains on pebbly material.

Hengistbury Head survives by a quirk of nature between the old and new mouths of the River Stour. Its abundant ironstone nodules nearly caused its destruction. In 1848 Holloway, a Christchurch coalman, began dredging ironstones just off-shore. The nodules were abundant around the Beer Pan rocks which may mark an earlier coastline. He used the nodules as profitable ballast for coal ships returning to South Wales—they contain about 30 per cent iron ore. Unfortunately the protective value of the doggers was not realised, erosion followed and the shore receded 9m annually until dredging stopped in 1856. Around the corner at Mudeford the same period was one of remarkable spit growth. Erosion continued more slowly after 1856, up to the building of the long groyne in 1938. While saving Hengistbury, the groyne reversed conditions to the east, cutting off much of the protective sand supply and increasing erosion at Highcliffe and Barton.

Beyond the long groyne the east shore is still littered with ironstone nodules. Walk to the north-east of the headland and then return by the summit path. Half-way back to the lookout is a huge quarry. The marked terrace along the north slopes of the headland is all waste from this working which Holloway dug for ironstones, and nearly cut the headland in two.

HIGHCLIFFE TO CHEWTON BUNNY

The highest Tertiary beds seen in Dorset form the cliffs east of Mudeford. Vehicles can be parked at Avon Beach, 188923. The section begins again in Boscombe Sands, but soon a pebble bed and dingy green clays come in at the cliff top. These are the Lower

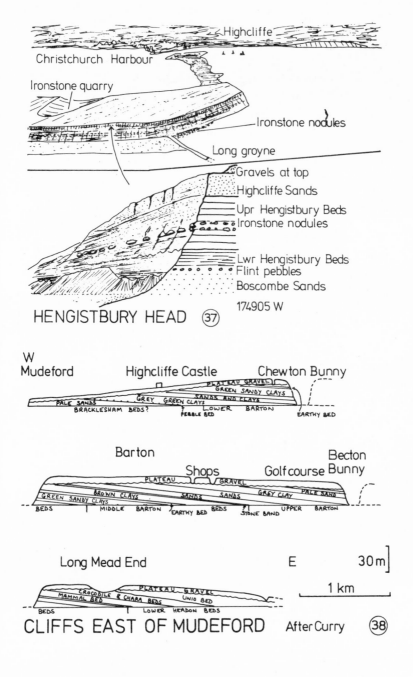

Highcliffe

Christchurch Harbour

Ironstone quarry

Ironstone nodules

Long groyne

Gravels at top
Highcliffe Sands
Upr Hengistbury Beds
Ironstone nodules

Lwr Hengistbury Beds
Flint pebbles
Boscombe Sands

174905 W

HENGISTBURY HEAD (37)

W
Mudeford   Highcliffe Castle   Chewton Bunny

PLATEAU GRAVEL
GREEN SANDY CLAYS
SANDS AND CLAYS
PALE SANDS   GREY GREEN CLAYS
BRACKLESHAM BEDS?   LOWER   BARTON
PEBBLE BED   EARTHY BED

Barton   Becton
Shops   Golf course Bunny

PLATEAU   GRAVEL
BROWN CLAYS   SANDS   SANDS   GREY CLAY   PALE SAND
GREEN SANDY CLAYS
BEDS   MIDDLE   BARTON   EARTHY BED   BEDS   STONE BAND   UPPER   BARTON

Long Mead End   E   30m

1 km

PLATEAU   GRAVEL
CROCODILE & CHARA BEDS   UNIO BED
MAMMAL BED
BEDS   LOWER HEADON BEDS

CLIFFS EAST OF MUDEFORD   After Curry   (38)

Barton Beds, equivalents of the Hengistbury Beds at the headland and, like them, followed by Highcliffe Sands. The latter take their name from the castle here, beneath which the easterly dip first brings them into the cliff top. The cliffs are very unstable and fine examples of slumping are seen below the castle in the crazy alignments of the trees. Figure 38 shows the coast succession, unfortunately destroyed by coast protection works east of the castle. Groynes and barriers make the beach hard going and it is best to follow one of the regraded terraces.

The Barton Beds are noted for their fossils, which occur prolifically in certain beds. At Chewton Bunny the junction of the Eocene Lower and Middle Barton Beds occurs. The junction actually appears about 9m up the cliff on the east side. 6m higher, or half-way up, lies the most spectacular horizon, the 1·5m Earthy Bed of the Middle Barton Beds, with turreted gastropods *Athleta luctator* and *Clavilithes* among its rich shell fauna.

CHAPTER 9

The Weymouth—Ringstead Bay Coast

Between Weymouth and Worbarrow Bay earth movements of Cretaceous and Tertiary age have brought together a variety of beds from different parts of the chronological sequence pursued so far. A short distance south of the present coast, the eastward-plunging anticline of the Weymouth area is replaced by the asymmetrical anticline of the Isle of Purbeck. The beds exposed in the modern cliffs reveal parts of both structures, and the intimate associations of beds produced are amply illustrated in numerous coves and cliff sections. The coast can be roughly divided into a western section, having mainly Jurassic beds—dealt with in the present chapter—and an eastern area, from White Nothe to Worbarrow Bay, where the white chalk beds are the major element (Chapter 10).

FURZY (OR JORDAN) CLIFF AND REDCLIFF POINT

The first cliffs east of Weymouth expose beds involved in the Weymouth anticline (Chapter 4). Due to the marshy ground of Radipole and Lodmoor masking the bulk of the outcrop, Furzy Cliff is the only east coast section of the Oxford Clays. The cliff lies in the *cordatum* zone—12m of Jordan Cliff Clays at the base and about 13m of Red Nodule Beds above. Ammonites in many cases are crushed white impressions, but in the Red Nodule Beds there are large *Gryphaea dilatata* and pockets of the ribbed oyster *Lopha gregarea*. The beds earn their name from the small cement-stone nodules coated with red iron oxide which occur in bands amid the grey clays. In 1972 parts of an *Ichthyosaurus* were discovered here, its thirty-eight vertebrae centra making it the largest such find ever from the Oxford Clays of Dorset.

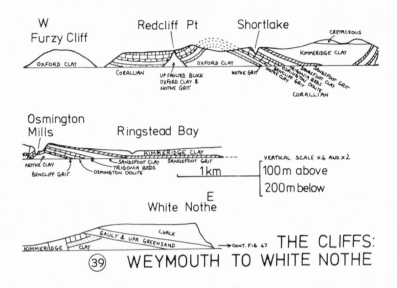

THE CLIFFS:
(39) WEYMOUTH TO WHITE NOTHE

Fault and fold features are involved in the interesting geology of Redcliffe Point (Figure 40). The change in direction of the coast at the point reveals that the apparently horizontal Corallian to the west is really a strike section along the southern limb of an anticline. In Ham Cliff, the new coastal direction cuts north through the fold and the Corallian Beds are seen arching upwards (Figure 40). The fold feature is large enough to bring the Oxford Clays up again in its core.

The Red Nodule Beds reappear and are also exposed again in the tip of Redcliff Point, being brought up by an east-west strike fault against Corallian Nothe Clays (Figure 40). The fault is best seen around the margins of the point. On the headland itself it is obscured by slumping and the similarity of colour between the Corallian and Oxford Clays. Notice the little spit of doggers curving east from the point and revealing the direction of longshore drift.

In the upper cliff, higher Corallian beds can be seen, the Osmington Oolite Series, with ripple marking, iron and lignitic material, and the oyster *Exogyra nana* occurring at several horizons.

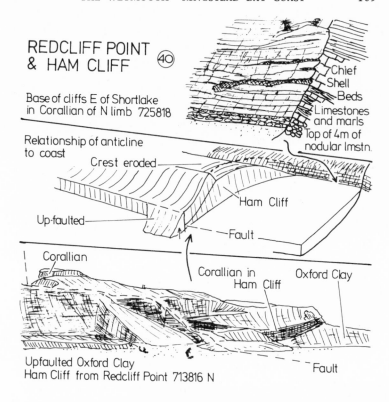

REDCLIFF POINT & HAM CLIFF (40)

Base of cliffs E of Shortlake in Corallian of N limb 725818

Chief Shell Beds
Limestones and marls
Top of 4m of nodular lmstn.

Relationship of anticline to coast
Crest eroded
Ham Cliff
Up-faulted
Fault

Corallian
Corallian in Ham Cliff
Oxford Clay

Upfaulted Oxford Clay
Ham Cliff from Redcliff Point 713816 N
Fault

OSMINGTON MILLS

East of Shortlake, the coast again becomes a strike section, but now along the northern limb of the Ham Cliff anticline. The eroded fold used to continue east to link up with the Ringstead anticline. The Corallian forms the base of its northward dipping remains, acting as a buttress to the receding Kimmeridge Clay slopes above it (Figure 40).

The most interesting item east of Black Head are the enormous mud slides which extend as far as Osmington Mills. We have now reached a point where the unconformable Cretaceous beds cap the cliffs, in a feature known as the Spring Bottom syncline—a down-fold perched high up in the ridge area between the present cliffs and an older Jurassic-bedded syncline of the Upton Valley inland. So the Kimmeridge Clay cliffs, seen here to be dipping north from

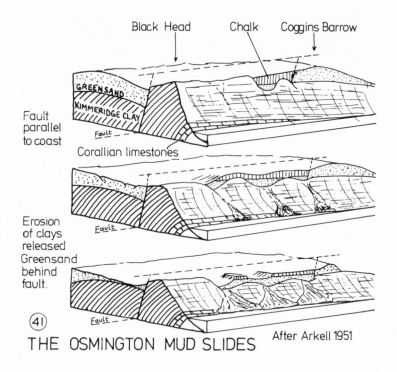

Black Head   Chalk   Coggins Barrow

Fault parallel to coast

GREENSAND
KIMMERIDGE CLAY
Fault

Corallian limestones

Erosion of clays released Greensand behind fault.

Fault

(41)   Fault

THE OSMINGTON MUD SLIDES   After Arkell 1951

the eroded Ham Cliff anticline, are in fact common to the limb of the Upton syncline as well. 'Mud glaciers' is the colourfully inaccurate name given to the flows which have tumbled seawards from them. They are the largest features of this kind anywhere along the British coast, so extensive that they pass from cliff slides to inland hill slips. They were formed on a spring night sometime between 1910 and 1914. Why did such spectacular movement occur here and nowhere else along the local cliffs? The clue to the movements is revealed in Figure 41. A fault, not shown in the current edition of map 342, runs parallel to and a short distance north of the coast. Known as the Spring Bottom Fault, it interrupts the north-dipping Corallian and Kimmeridge Clay and throws down the northern limb of the Cretaceous-bedded Spring Bottom syncline against them. Nothing resulted from this until coastal erosion had proceeded to the point where the receding Kimmeridge Clay slopes had retreated far enough to reveal the cliff top course of the fault. The Gault and porous Greensand beyond were virtually a reservoir behind a shrinking dam of Kimmeridge Clay, and eventually the clay could no longer contain them. The dam burst, the Greensand reservoir rock (reminiscent of Black Ven, Chapter 2) broke forward over the fault at three points where natural gullies had previously existed and set off the Kimmeridge Clay beyond in mud slides.

There are three features of interest at Osmington Mills itself. Firstly, about 236m west of the slipway there is a section through Nothe Clay, Bencliff Grit, Osmington Oolite and *Trigonia clavellata* Beds, all dipping 48° north into the cliff. Working back to the slipway there is slipped and faulted Kimmeridge Clay, produced by another east-west fault which is named the Picnic Inn Fault because it passes beneath the inn (now renamed the Smugglers Rest). The slumping obscures the fault's outcrop in the cliffs. A second feature, which can be observed seawards of the clay at low tide, is a number of smaller faults and folds in foreshore of Corallian beds.

Thirdly, examine the area of the little knoll adjacent to the slipway. This little triangular hill appears to be fault-bounded to west and south, although it may be a fallen mass. Left between the coast and the stream, it exposes Nothe Grits at its base and these form the prominent ledge over which the stream cascades to the beach. Due to the fault, the Nothe Clay on the south is missing and the south face of the knoll then rises through Bencliff Grit and Osmington Oolite beds, the former full of burrow markings.

BRAN POINT

Towards Bran Point the slump-damaged coast gradually fills the beach with huge brown sandstone doggers from the Bencliff Grit. Vertical cliffs appear again near Frenchman's Ledge where the stumps of an old wreck act as a useful marker in the study of Corallian exposures around the Bran Point fault. This is yet another east-west fault, parallel to the coast, its significance being that it just cuts the edge of the beach at Bran Point. Since the fault downthrows north, the seaward ledges are all higher in the succession than those apparently opposite them in the cliff face.

Figure 42 shows the cliff succession and maps the contrast between this and the sea ledges. The area must be studied at low tide when the fault can be located accurately at the steplike inner margin of Bran Ledge immediately in front of the point. In the cliff the easterly dip successively brings all the beds within reach as the student continues east into Ringstead Bay. There is a second opportunity to collect from the *Trigonia clavellata* Beds previously examined in Sandsfoot Castle Cove, Weymouth, and oil seepages may be noted here and there in the faces.

BRAN POINT FAULT
42

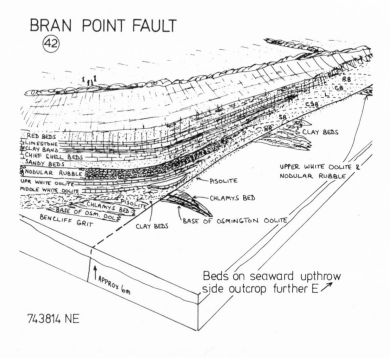

743814 NE

RINGSTEAD BAY

Ringstead Bay begins unspectacularly when approached from its western shore, giving little hint of the impressive cliff scenery to come or the range of geological delights it holds. Its western cliffs are low and much slumped due to the Ringstead Waxy Clays which follow the Corallian Beds from The Glen eastwards. The Ringstead Coral Bed can be located in this unpromising jumble, however. Its corals are species of *Thecosmilia* and *Thamnasteria,* but there are also many serpulae, lamellibranchs and pectens. Spines of the sea-urchin *Cidaris* may also be discovered.

Continue east along the beach. The Ringstead Ledges exposed at low tide are Corallian Beds just south of the Bran Point fault. The *Trigonia clavellata* Beds and the nodular rubble are both seen. Cross to the eastern end of the bay (Figure 43). The Corallian Beds have disappeared there due to easterly plunge of the Ringstead Bay anticline and its core is now occupied by the Kimmeridge Clay. The crest and south side of the fold have been eroded by the great Cretaceous unconformity which is magnificently displayed here. The Upper Greensand and Chalk outcrops cut down across the top of the anticline towards the shore below White Nothe and the Kimmeridge Clay passes inland beneath them, to remain hidden for 11km until Gad Cliff is reached.

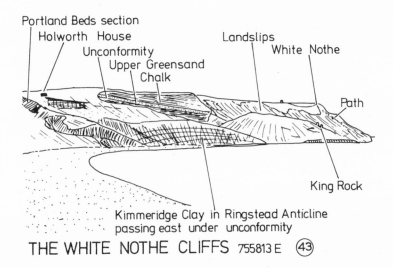

THE WHITE NOTHE CLIFFS 755813 E ㊸

There is little Kimmeridge Clay to be seen beyond the eastern end of the beach at Ringstead due to slips from the unconformable chalk above, but about 23m is visible behind the beach, belonging to the *Subplanites* zone. A prominent White Band near the top may be the lowest of the three seen east of Rope Lake Head (Figure

16). All the fossils are preserved as the white and pearly fragments typical of the clays. The ammonite *Subplanites* and the brachiopod *Lucina* are the main finds. There are Blackstone beds here too as at Kimmeridge, their presence being the cause of the local name Burning Cliff which applies to the upper part west of Holworth House. There, due to a north-south fault, the White Stone Band is upthrown to cliff-top height. In the Blackstone horizons beneath it heat released by decaying pyrite material caused spontaneous combustion in 1826, the cliff continuing to smoulder for several years.

Climb up to the Portland–Purbeck bed exposure below Holworth Chapel. These beds are on the downthrown side of the north-south Burning Cliff fault and at their base the upper part of the Kimmeridge Clay is exposed now and then—adding another 56m to its Ringstead succession. Slumping may make this exposure awkward but the student will fare better on the Portland–Purbeck Beds above (Figure 44). Although their attitude suggests they are part of the Ringstead anticline, these beds are believed to be faulted into position here. The problem cannot be unravelled however, the clues being hidden under the Cretaceous unconformity, slips and the sea.

The Holworth House section is important, revealing a full sequence of the Portland Stone and an affinity with Isle of Portland exposures rather than those of Purbeck. Due to the steep dip it is best to move around on the rough scree slopes and move in on the level to each individual bed you wish to examine. The first bed visible at the base is usually a 1·5m cementstone in the Portland Sands. A 0·5m black clay occurs 0.7m above it and the top of the Portland Sands comes 1·2m higher still.

The Basal Shell Bed of the Portland Stone Cherty Series which follows is less weathered here than at the West Weares on Portland but its 0·6m is full of shells preserved in calcite, including *Trigonia*. Examine the weathered face of a 1·5m bed which follows. It is covered with worm burrows of *Serpula gordialis* which stand out because they are more resistant than the enclosing rock. In an overhang at the top of this bed are the broken remains of a large ammonite. Work up through the rest of the Cherty Series, noticing how the cherts become smaller, more brown and splintery. 8m above the serpula bed is the base of the Freestone Series, forming an alcove in the section since, even on such an awkward site as this, its lowest 3·5m has been quarried. From the roach above, *Isognomon listeri* can be obtained, but the most fossiliferous Freestone Series bed here is the Top Roach Bed, 3m above the quarried alcove. It is a mass of *Laevitrigonia gibbosa, Protocardia dissimilis* and species of *Pleuromya, Lima* and *Chlamys*.

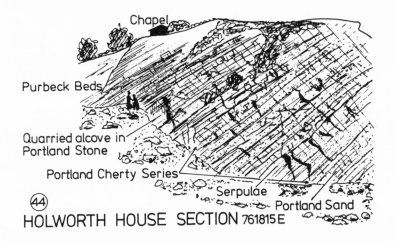

HOLWORTH HOUSE SECTION 761815 E

Being thinner and more varied, the Lower Purbeck Beds degrade more easily and are more difficult to examine. The lowest bed is cemented firmly on to the Freestone roach and is full of hollow moulds of freshwater snails, the gastropods *Hydrobia, Valvata, Cyrena*. Bonded onto this bed is a 15cm tufaceous limestone with ostracods (page 90). Two thin limestones follow, each resting on a thin Dirt Bed. Higher up a 5cm chert seam has some trace of Broken Bed development above it.

Return to the base of the section and scramble up over the ridge to the east. From its crest there is a magnificent view of the unconformity. Away up to the left the Upper Greensand can be clearly picked out, and nearer ground on the left is a relic of its basal surface.

WHITE NOTHE

A circular walk can be made along the cliff top from Sea Barn Farm to White Nothe, then (and only if you have a head for heights) down the zig-zag path and back through the landslips to Ringstead Bay, coming back up via the section described above. By keeping close to the fence east of Holworth House it is possible to examine the top beds of the Upper Greensand as they reach the cliff top. Access is not easy generally, however, and this is a problem since these cliffs are the best developed and best exposed section of the top beds in Dorset. The beds are very phosphatised, a feature indicating that the beds were formed in fairly deep anaerobic water, their fossils being forms that lived higher in the Greensand seas and fell into the sediment on death. The beds contain a rich ammonite fauna, particularly in a bed 4·2m below the top. Collecting from the bed and from the Cenomanian basement bed at the base of the chalk, which also has a prolific fauna here, is best left until later when the landslip can be explored for fallen blocks. Remember that it is the Upper Greensand which is seen here (Albian unconformity, Chapter 1). The Lower Greensand is only just present at Lulworth and is overlapped in all these areas farther west.

The cliff scenery of White Nothe recalls Black Ven and Stonebarrow in West Dorset. Successive landslips, nearly all rotational shears, have turned the undercliff into a cascade of giant steps. About seven major blocks can be counted.

Along the edge of the uppermost block, gingery-brown coloured angular flint gravel which caps so much of the downlands is exposed. In the Dorset Downs the normal cover of the chalk is Clay-with-Flints. The latter is found on all the broad areas of downland, but towards the margin, in valley-side situations and along cliffs such as White Nothe, run-off is more rapid and the enclosing clay material has been washed away, leaving the angular gravel instead.

The views from the top of White Nothe are breathtaking. Here the student can see the two great anticlinal structures of South Dorset, to the west the denuded Weymouth anticline and the great fragment of its limb, Portland; to the east, the asymmetrical anticline of Purbeck.

From the top of the headland a steep zig-zag path leads down to the shore, passing down from *coranguinum* zone chalk at the cliff top through barren *cortestudinarium* zone beds. The only reasonably fossiliferous zone is the next one down, the *planus* zone, visible in bluffs below the cliff top lookout; there, by climbing over loose rock slopes, calcareous sponges may be found. Do not confuse the *planus* zone, *Holaster planus* and the *plenus* Marl which occurs lower down the succession at the top of the Cenomanian or Lower Chalk and gets its name from its characteristic belemnite, *Actinocamax plenus* (see Table of Strata).

The features to be seen in the undercliff are the 13·7m of evenly-bedded Lower Chalk forming the point of White Nothe and the shore ledges, with the *plenus* Marl the white smooth bed above it, and some of the exposures in the landslipped area to the west. Make for King Rock, the distinctive mass with two natural rock sculptures on top of it, where the Cenomanian or Lower Chalk and the top of the Upper Greensand are exposed. The basement bed of the former yields ammonites, echinoids (sea-urchins) and brachiopods. Having examined the exposure, search the landslips for further fallen blocks of it.

CHAPTER 10

White Nothe—Worbarrow Bay Coast

East of White Nothe the coast is dominated by the high margin of the chalk downlands. In a county of geological superlatives this area takes pride of place for structural interest since it exposes the western limits of the Purbeck anticline but without solving many of the intriguing questions associated with it. Wedged between the downlands and the sea are narrow outcrops of Wealden, Portland and Purbeck Beds, all tilted at high angles, their continuity interrupted by the modern bays and cliffs.

WHITE NOTHE TO BAT'S HEAD

The beaches and cliffs from White Nothe to Bat's Head, below West and Middle Bottoms, are inaccessible except by boat. A solution to this problem is to take a cruise from Weymouth to Lulworth since the boats keep close to the shore from White Nothe onwards, providing excellent views of the cliffs. Attention must focus on the area immediately east of White Nothe since it is the crucial meeting point of the Weymouth and Purbeck anticlines.

The Weymouth structure disappears at White Nothe, but the Purbeck fold comes out in the cliff, being detected by the lines of flints within the chalk. These dip east at first towards Middle Bottom, but start to rise sharply in the cliffs towards Bat's Head where the beds become vertical (Figure 45). Note that there is no trace of a Ballard Down type fault, page 98.

Notice the offshore rocks near Bat's Head—remnants of an east-west Portland Stone outcrop still seen in Durdle Door and forming the bastions of the cliffs at Dungy Head, Lulworth Cove, Mupe and Worbarrow Bays. Like the cliff exposures, these off-

THE PURBECK FOLD AT BAT'S HEAD ㊺

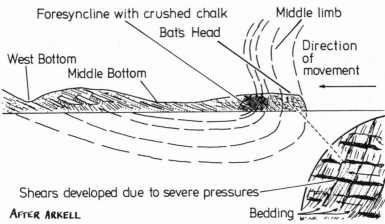

Foresyncline with crushed chalk   Middle limb

Bat's Head

West Bottom

Middle Bottom

Direction
of
movement

Shears developed due to severe pressures

AFTER ARKELL

Bedding

GEOLOGY OF THE WHITE NOTHE AREA w ㊻

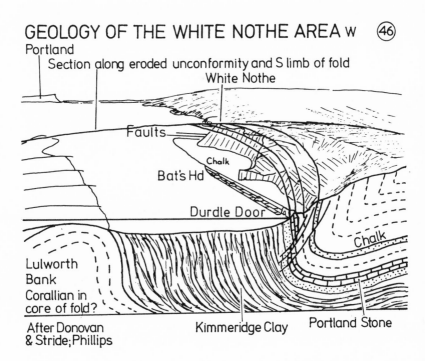

Portland

Section along eroded unconformity and S limb of fold

White Nothe

Faults

Chalk

Bat's Hd

Durdle Door

Chalk

Lulworth
Bank
Corallian in
core of fold?

After Donovan
& Stride; Phillips

Kimmeridge Clay   Portland Stone

shore islets have steep northerly dips, around 80° in the middle limb of the fold. The intriguing problem is where did the Portland outcrop go farther west? Submarine accoustic surveys suggest that the Portland Beds are overlapped by the chalk unconformity 180m west of the last islet (Figure 46), and that additional north-south faults occur in the Holworth House area. These would be tear faults, linking the islet outcrops to the section west of Holworth House and in turn to more westerly ones.

The area has always been a puzzle to geologists. How could the Purbeck fold, still a major structure here as the chalk cliffs confirm, disappear without trace just west of them? Was its axis taken up by the Weymouth anticline to which it seems to be aligned? And, if so, how?—since the one is so sharply asymmetrical and the other plunging eastwards. A fold is commonly replaced by another en echelon with it and the tear fault idea may explain the disappearance of the Purbeck anticline, displacing the structures north to be continued along the north side of the Weymouth

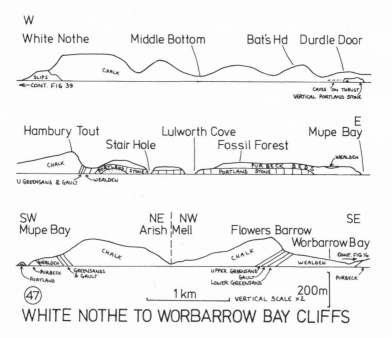

WHITE NOTHE TO WORBARROW BAY CLIFFS

lowland in the complex Ridgeway–Abbotsbury fault zone (Chapter 15).

A second possibility, put forward earlier, is the existence of an important Tertiary reversed fault, replacing the Purbeck structure to seawards and linking up with the Radipole Fault of the Weymouth area. The problem will certainly continue to exercise attention for years to come since sea-bed sediment makes underwater study in Weymouth Bay difficult and it is not known what takes place in older beds beneath White Nothe.

DURDLE COVE

Dominated by its enormous natural arch of Portland Stone, Durdle Cove is one of the most beautiful in Dorset. Survival of the stone here protects the less resistant Purbeck, Wealden and Greensand beds which form the narrow col of land separating the cove from Man O'War Cove beyond. Figures 49 and 50 show the geology of the cove and the view westward from it. In the recess of Scratchy Bottom part of the *coranguinum* zone of the chalk is exposed. Working east—ie down the succession—the side of the recess is in the *cortestudinarium* zone, not very fossiliferous but yielding echinoids *Micraster* and *Echinocorys*. Between the outer edge of the recess and the cove the chalk face is mainly in the *planus* zone, with a remarkable line of sea caves.

The sea caves have formed along a thrust dipping south out of the cliff. The chalk beds were severely folded during the formation of the Purbeck anticline, accommodating the stresses by shearing and thrusting. Three major groups of shears are recognised in the Dorset chalk—Group 1 dip 60–70° south and are the oldest, formed in the overturned middle limb of the anticline. Figure 48 shows how the older beds would tend to ride up relative to the younger, thus creating these shears and Group 2—a minor set dipping 50–70° north—at the same time.

When the fold had reached its maximum extent and could not fold any further, continued pressures developed the third group dipping 25–40° south; occasionally, as here at the sea caves, becoming true thrust-planes with a 0–20° south dip. Note the

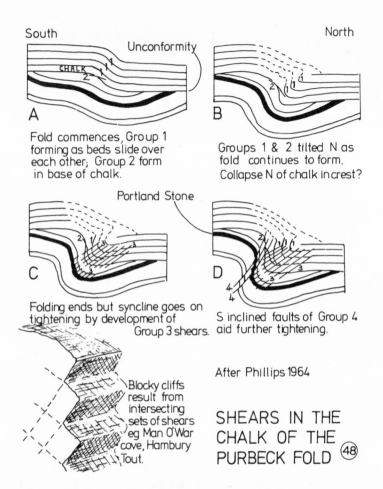

South   Unconformity   North

CHALK

A

Fold commences, Group 1 forming as beds slide over each other; Group 2 form in base of chalk.

B

Groups 1 & 2 tilted N as fold continues to form. Collapse N of chalk in crest?

Portland Stone

C

Folding ends but syncline goes on tightening by development of Group 3 shears.

D

S inclined faults of Group 4 aid further tightening.

After Phillips 1964

Blocky cliffs result from intersecting sets of shears eg Man O'War cove, Hambury Tout.

SHEARS IN THE CHALK OF THE PURBECK FOLD ⑱

thrust breccia exposed in the caves. As Figure 48 shows, these shear groups account for much of the detailed form of the chalk cliffs along this coast. Further groups of shears are Group 4, reversed faults dipping 70–90° south (an example occurs in Lulworth Cove, below) and Group 5 which are reversed faults overthrust south and dipping 35–55° north.

Durdle Cove is the first exposure revealing the behaviour of beds beneath the chalk as we move east. As Figure 49 shows, it is a small cove and, remembering the long sections in Durlston and Swanage Bays, it is obvious that the succession is much reduced here. The reduction is partly explained by thinning of the Wealden beds west through Purbeck, but examination of the succession soon shows that more than thinning is involved. Considerable sequences of beds are missing. The cause is strike faulting, running nearly parallel to the coast and slicing through the Durdle headland. Begin in the corner adjacent to the Portland Stone outer wall. Bands of limestone and shale are eroded into a narrow alcove at the most southerly part normally accessible. A hard limestone rib follows as the explorer moves back towards the steps and 5·5m beyond it the Cherty Freshwater Limestone can be found. The Cinder Bed, 0·8m beyond again, is only 0·9m compared to its 2·6m in Durlston Bay. Between it and the steps is a shattered area of beef beds with grey-coloured cone-in-cone calcite freely available. Obviously much of the Middle Purbeck is faulted out since we have reached these beds in such a short distance, and

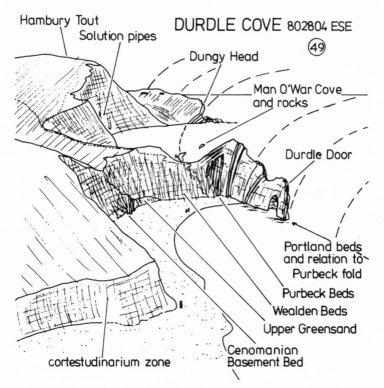

Hambury Tout
Solution pipes
DURDLE COVE 802804 ESE
(49)
Dungy Head
Man O'War Cove
and rocks
Durdle Door
Portland beds
and relation to
Purbeck fold
Purbeck Beds
Wealden Beds
Upper Greensand
Cenomanian
Basement Bed
cortestudinarium zone

there is little evidence of either Lower or Upper Building Stones here (see succession, page 87). The whole of the Upper Purbeck is missing also for as soon as the steps are crossed Wealden Beds are encountered. The Wealden Beds reveal cross-bedding, river channels (all up on end, remember) and brown lignitic material from plant debris washed in by them. The sands are well up the thinner Wealden sequence; the lower Wealden is also faulted out. The faults must be hidden in the slumped material of the headland.

Little is visible of the rest of the Wealden present. At least 90m of Upper Wealden was removed before the Gault and Upper Greensand were deposited over this area anyway—another reason for the thin succession. The Upper Greensand is also obscured until the student reaches the well-developed Exogyra Sandstones near the top of it. The undersides of these beds form the first vertical outcrops on the north side of the cove. Examine the Exogyra rock for the oysters which name it, for *Pecten* and small echinoids. The beds are very cherty, forming vertical ribs with gullies in intervening clayey beds. Worn smooth, the latter give little hint of the well-preserved fossils they contain. In the top clayey bed, generally high up in the inaccessible part of the outcrop, fossils may be seen weathering out. Nautili up to 30cm

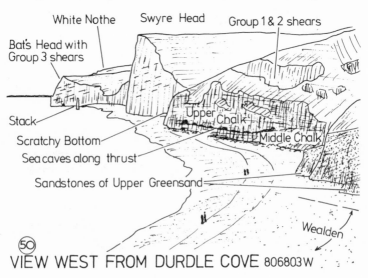

VIEW WEST FROM DURDLE COVE 806803W

diameter have been found in the stone bed dividing the top two clay layers.

Continuing north around the Upper Greensand ribs, the base of the chalk (Cenomanian basement bed) is easily distinguished on colour alone. It is fossiliferous, but once again the accessible areas near the beach suffer too much attention. In the recess behind, two Group 3 shears can be seen cutting the *plenus* Marl. The marl yields few of the belemnites which name it.

MAN O'WAR COVE

The col between Durdle Cove and Man O'War Cove is the kind of place where you could sit for hours admiring the views. The scene eastwards is nearly a mirror image of the one to the west, the Portland Stone again an eroded reef, heading towards the next outcrop at Dungy Head. Purbeck and Wealden are exposed in the cliffs below, the Wealden having already increased in thickness from 49m in Durdle Cove to 65m here. The Wealden is better exposed here, particularly the quartz grit which has attracted unwelcome initial carving. On the inner cliffs of the cove intersecting shears of Groups 1 and 2 cause the cliff to erode in blocks. Man O'War Point, a small projection to the east, makes low tide essential before making the shore walk to St Oswald's Bay. The point is a significant spot. There the distance between the chalk and the eroded Portland Stone reefs is at its smallest anywhere along the coast, leaving only 76m for the Purbeck and Wealden outcrops.

Continuing eastwards, the cliff is remarkable for its enormous solution holes, the name Red Hole graphically describing the red iron straining which is such a feature of them. The sediment in them also includes grey sands and ground-up flints. The material is probably Eocene in age like the heathland sands and gravels. The pipes are amazingly deep; the largest reaches 121m below the present hill top at Hambury Tout. If the pipes were formed before the chalk reached its present vertical attitude ie, as it was folded, they could well have been 182m deep, the upper parts being removed later with erosion of the crest of the fold.

The eastern end of St Oswald's Bay provides the third section across the Purbeck fold structure along this coast. The shore below Dungy Head resembles Gad Cliff farther east, the Portland Stone rising to expose the Portland Sands below. Erosion of the latter has undermined the Cherty and Stone Series, littering the shore with huge fallen blocks. Specimens of the ammonite *Glaucolithites* are visible in the sands. This is also another locality for *Serpula gordialis* and *Exogyra nana*. Notice the fine series of open tension gashes near the top of the Portland Stone.

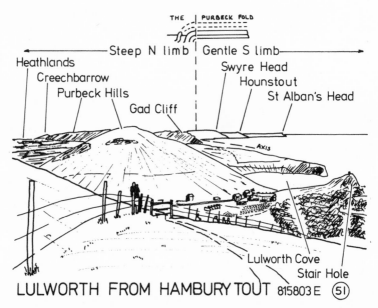

LULWORTH FROM HAMBURY TOUT 815803 E (51)

STAIR HOLE AND THE LULWORTH CRUMPLE

W. J. Arkell called Purbeck 'the most interesting and the most perfectly exposed of all the folds thrown up across the chalk plains of North-West Europe by the Alpine orogeny. In the cliffs of the Dorset coast the sea has laid bare all parts of the structure from the core or crestal region through the vertical and over-turned limb of the foresyncline into the foreland where the Cretaceous sits with sharp unconformity upon previously folded and eroded Jurassic formations'. Excitement must be compounded on excitement when the student continues to Stair Hole and Lulworth for there many of the upturned and faulted beds seen so far are intriguingly bound up with the rucking of the Lulworth Crumple. The crumple recalls the similar feature in the marble beds of Peveril Point. Another will be seen at Kingston (Chapter 12). The Lulworth Crumple is better exposed and examined at Stair Hole.

Stair Hole is a modern example of how the local coast received its detailed shape. Here the sea has eroded through joints in the Portland Stone, widening them into arches. The most westerly have already collapsed into the sea to form an open gap. Once the limestone wall is breached the Purbeck and Wealden behind it are soon removed. Much of this erosion is due to the Wealden's inherent instability. Great slips and flows occur as the inner slopes tumble over each other to present themselves to the sea for destruction and are then sucked away through the arches. The same process accounts for St Oswald's Bay, Lulworth Cove, Mupe and Worbarrow Bays—once the originally continuous outcrop of Portland Beds between Durdle Door and Gad cliff was breached. A parallel case may be drawn with the breaching of the former chalk outcrop between Ballard Down and The Needles, Isle of Wight. Once that had been destroyed, less resistant Tertiary beds were similarly removed from the area between Poole Harbour and The Solent.

Stair Hole has created fine sections in the Purbeck Beds—Middle and Upper are present but part of the Lower Purbeck has been faulted out. The east face is the best exposed (Figure 52), its structures clearly minor features above the steeply north-dipping Portland Beds. It is generally accepted that the Purbeck Beds behaved as a weak formation when the folding occurred and that their Broken Beds were partly the result of shattering during fold movements (page 85). Like the features at Peveril Point and Kingston, the Lulworth Crumple seems to be yet another example of their incompetence, but the puzzle is how did it form? Two principal ideas have been put forward.

The first theory is based on the fact that when beds are folded, those on the inside of the bend produced must reduce in length to

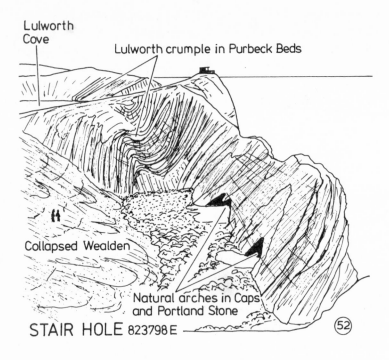

Lulworth Cove

Lulworth crumple in Purbeck Beds

Collapsed Wealden

Natural arches in Caps and Portland Stone

STAIR HOLE 823798 E

52

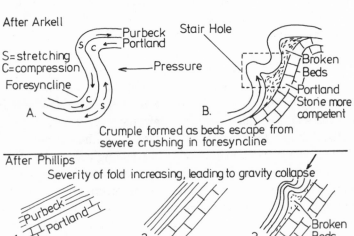

After Arkell

S = stretching
C = compression

Foresyncline

Purbeck
Portland

Pressure

A.

Stair Hole

Broken Beds

Portland Stone more competent

B.

Crumple formed as beds escape from severe crushing in foresyncline

After Phillips

Severity of fold increasing, leading to gravity collapse

Purbeck
Portland

1.

2.

3.

Broken Beds

Portland acting as slide plane

THE LULWORTH CRUMPLE

53

accommodate the fold while those on the outside are stretched (Figure 53A). The idea suggested is that in the foresyncline of the acute Purbeck fold (this part is below present visible level here) the Purbeck Beds were under such a shortening pressure that they could not stand it and had to escape upwards and outwards to form the crumple Figure 53B. Against the idea is the fact that the beds on the inside of the bend there would have been on the *outside* at the crest of the fold, an area of stretching, and this would have absorbed the stresses. Perhaps, however, the crest had already been eroded away during the growth of the fold.

The second theory concerning the Lulworth Crumple proposes gravity sliding as the mechanism—the increasing steepness of the Portland Beds in the fold eventually raising the Purbecks to an angle where downward failure occurred, forcing out the ruck-like crumple. The lower part of Figure 53 illustrates the three stages in this process. As the figures show it can also explain the development of the shear systems and the faulting out of the missing beds in the Durdle promontory. These faults were developed as thrust-faults by the continued northward movement of the Portland Stone. Acting as a steep and more rigid ram it was able to put the chalk up into even steeper dips, eventually overturning it. At the back of Lulworth curious dip readings of 108° north are the result.

The western section at Stair Hole does not display the crumple so well. The feature is partly hidden under grassy slopes at the top of the face, but note its higher position there, ie the feature does dip eastward. Traced into Lulworth it appears lower still on the west side of the cove and only just above sea level on the east side.

LULWORTH COVE

On reaching the beach, the first cliffs are in the Upper Greensand. Look for some brickwork of an old limekiln. The Greensand outcrop ends just beyond it. In the Chalk which follows, the *plenus* Marl is readily identifiable, cut out upwards by a Group 5 fault. The rest of the back of the cove is in Middle Chalk dipping 40–60° north, but about two-thirds of the way up the cliff face an undulating break can be traced—the outcrop of a Group 4 fault, and above it are beds of Upper Chalk, overturned and dipping 108° north! Cross the degraded eastern outcrops of the Greensand and Wealden—ignoring for the moment the pathway to the Fossil Forest and Mupe Bay—and examine the Lulworth Crumple again.

A small point on the east shore is formed by the Cinder Bed and the Cherty Freshwater Limestone. In these thicker beds the crumple appears as a sharp downturn near the base of the cliff. Further small disturbances can be seen in beds beyond and below it in the succession. At the far end of the beach there is an excellent section in the Broken Beds and access can be gained to the projecting eastern arm of the cove by walking up the bedding surface of the Portland Beds. This is a good vantage point to admire all the geological features of the cove. Although the various bays and coves of this part of Dorset cut north into the rock sequence, giving numerous dip sections, here the student is reminded that the coast is a strike section. From Durdle Door to Gad Cliff, the originally continuous outcrops and the coast run parallel. Return to the beach and take the path eastwards up the Wealden outcrop to the army range gate.

THE FOSSIL FOREST

From Lulworth to Kimmeridge the coast has been a subject of controversy for many years on account of that mixed blessing, the army. Undoubtedly the coast is one of the finest in Britain and, little by little over recent years, the public have been given greater access to it. Much of the land seawards of the chalk ridge is enclosed for safety reasons in case of overshooting or ricocheting of shells from the heathland ranges to the north. The arguments have always been finely balanced and it would require a King Solomon to judge them. On the army's credit side are local civilian employment, a great increase in wildlife (which finds humanity more lethal than shells) and protection of some fine geology from the thoughtless abuse so many sections suffer. A National Park status will be essential protection whenever the ranges are removed. On the debit side it must be fairly stated that the irritation in being unable to go there at will for geological studies, or to walk and enjoy the superb scenery, has been gradually reduced in recent years. Fenced paths were opened to the Fossil Forest and Mupe Bay, and access allowed to Tyneham and Worbarrow Bay, at first, in August only, but later every weekend. Now at last the full distance from Lulworth to Kimmeridge has been opened, thus completing the Dorset Coast Path from Lyme Regis to Shell Bay, near Poole. The newly opened sections in the range area are, of course, subject to range-firing activities, but are generally open every weekend and in August. The path keeps close to the cliffs everywhere, except at Arish Mell. There it is fenced because of the danger present, but elsewhere the new sections are waymarked and *unfenced*. Fine views are obtained, but they must *not* tempt you off the pathway. Continuation of the arrangement obviously depends on the good sense of all who use the pathway.

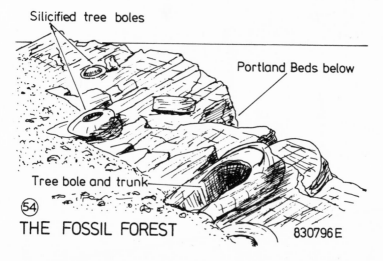

Silicified tree boles

Portland Beds below

Tree bole and trunk

54

THE FOSSIL FOREST   830796 E

So do *keep strictly to the marked path everywhere.* Leaving Lulworth Cove turn first right along the one to the Fossil Forest.

Part of a strike section in the Purbeck Beds, the Forest occupies a ledge formed by the Hard Cap. 0·6–1·2m below it in the cliff the Dirt Beds are exposed with the Portland Stone beneath them. Above the ledge there is another fine exposure of the Broken Beds which extend higher up the succession here than anywhere else, into the Cypris Freestones.

At the edge of the ledge examine the good Dirt Bed exposures. These fossil soils contain many fragments and pebbles of limestone. It is Portland Stone material, yet at every known outcrop the Portland Beds beneath are not eroded, so possibly the fragments were washed into or with the soil from unknown sources.

The surface of the Hard Cap is the Fossil Forest horizon. Hammering or collecting is *forbidden* here. Use the camera to record the tufa-encrusted boles or burrs which mark the base of former conifers. One or two fallen trunks can also be seen. Cut down their length they resemble round troughs. The burrs are open centred in some cases, in others not. The wood preserved in them is silicified, showing its detailed structures. The Fossil Forest is the best permanent exposure of these tree remains, of course, but similar features occur in Portland quarries, if you happen to be there at the right time and are told where to look.

The long strike section of the Broken Beds should also be examined. Little structure can be seen, the blocks of limestone are brittle in fracture and vary greatly in size. Generally their long axis is along the strike.

MUPE BAY

For those prepared to walk, Mupe Bay provides a quiet beach on crowded summer days. The enclosure near the far end of the range path overlooks Bacon Hole where the Purbeck Beds are again exposed in section. The outcrop of Portland Beds continues as the eroded line of Mupe Rocks, easily linked visually with the outcrops in Worbarrow Tout opposite.

On reaching the beach, the ledges to the south can be explored at low tide as far as Bacon Hole. The Cherty Freshwater Limestone and Cinder Bed can be located just around the corner. The Bacon Hole–Mupe Bay section is the most complete one from Portland Stone through Purbeck Beds in existence. If the tide allows, examine the Broken Beds closely and a series of asymmetric folds may be seen in the Cypris Freestones above them—again, these

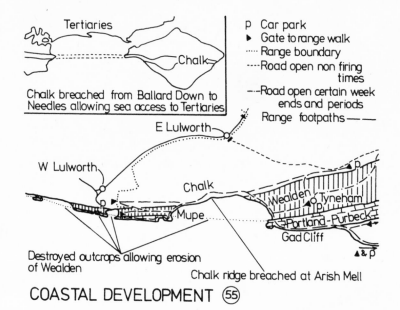

Tertiaries

Chalk

Chalk breached from Ballard Down to
Needles allowing sea access to Tertiaries

p Car park
▶ Gate to range walk
····· Range boundary
---- Road open non firing
          times
-·-Road open certain week
      ends and periods
Range footpaths ——

E Lulworth

W Lulworth

Chalk

Mupe

Wealden   Tyneham

Portland-Purbeck

Gad Cliff

Destroyed outcrops allowing erosion
of Wealden

Chalk ridge breached at Arish Mell

COASTAL DEVELOPMENT ⑤⑤

have been quoted in favour of both explanations of the Lulworth
Crumple.

Progression from bay to bay along the local coast reveals a
thicker succession at each successive one, and consequently a
larger bay. In addition the Purbeck and Wealden are also free of
reductions due to faulting, suffered farther west. The Wealden
increase is particularly significant in enlarging bay sizes for it is
in this outcrop that erosion occurs more easily. Mupe and Worbarrow Bays have now combined to form a double oval, a forecast
of the future of Lulworth and Stair Hole. In Mupe and Worbarrow the Wealden is well exposed and forms a useful exercise
in the measuring and correlation of outcrops. North of the beach
path at Mupe the first beds seen are still in Purbeck material,
containing much lignite, the latter amazingly peatlike still con-
sidering its age and involvement in the Purbeck fold. About 19·5m
north, now in Wealden Beds, there is a strong odour from the
cliffs where about 5m of sands are coloured brown and impregnated
by oil. Boulders from these beds have greasy black coatings of it.
Ironstone beds stand out as dyke-like ribs, a 1m one making a ready

marker bed for correlation with the Worbarrow section and just beyond it is the coarse quartz grit previously seen at Durdle. Here the grit contains drifted plant debris, converted to lignite. At the northern end of the bay the Greensand, both Lower and Upper now, is obscured by slumping. From a mere 15cm trace on the east side of Lulworth Cove, the Lower Greensand has increased eastward to 20m here. The beach ends against the chalk ridge. Zones up to *Micraster coranguinum* are present, following the cliff into Arish Mell, but all poorly fossiliferous. By vehicle a return to Lulworth and then a circular journey over Whiteways Hill and Tyneham is necessary to reach Worbarrow Bay opposite. On foot follow the path through the ranges if they are open.

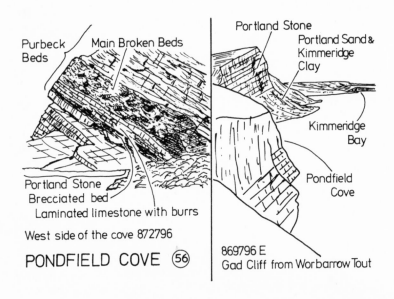

Purbeck Beds / Main Broken Beds

Portland Stone
Brecciated bed
Laminated limestone with burrs

West side of the cove 872796

PONDFIELD COVE (56)

Portland Stone
Portland Sand & Kimmeridge Clay

Kimmeridge Bay

Pondfield Cove

869796 E
Gad Cliff from Worbarrow Tout

WORBARROW TOUT AND BAY

Walking down from Tyneham car park, the slope to the left is the dipping upper surface of the Purbeck Beds. The slope ends in an irregular skyline, the jagged summit of Gad Cliff whose superb form can be appreciated from Pondfield Cove. The east face of the cove shows how erosion of the underlying Kimmeridge Clays and Portland Sand has caused falls of Portland Stone and Purbeck material. Around the cove and in the cliffs of the adjacent Worbarrow Tout there are good exposures of Purbeck Beds with Portland beneath. The best of these sections is in the Lower Purbeck Beds on the west side (Figure 56).

The north and west faces of Worbarrow Tout, cut back in a series of embayments, reveal the rest of the Purbeck Beds. Their total of 88m here continues the eastward thickening though it is still considerably less than the 121m in Durlston Bay. The Cinder Bed is well exposed and the succession is easily visible up to the Unio Beds which outcrop by the old slipway. Higher beds and the passage into the Wealden are concealed by slumping.

The cliffs of Worbarrow Bay reveal nearly 426m of Wealden sands, clays and grits. In sunny weather it might aptly be renamed Rainbow Bay. Because of the northerly dip the student must cover a good deal more than 426m to examine the section. As at Mupe Bay, several ironstone beds will be noticed. The grey quartz grit is almost exactly in the middle of the succession here.

At the northern end of the bay the Wealden Beds give way to the Lower Greensand, Gault and Upper Greensand, again poorly exposed at beach level due to slumping. The Upper Greensand is exposed in the higher cliff below Flowers Barrow, but unfortunately the exposure lies between the permitted access areas of the beach and the new cliff top pathway. Continuing along the shore, the chalk is glauconitic at first like the Greensand. The Lower (Cenomanian) and Middle (Turonian) Chalk are exposed near Cow Corner and small, rather clayey ammonite casts can be collected from the base of the Cenomanian.

We now come to the geology of inland South Dorset (Chapters 11–14), again in chronological order as far as possible, with more structurally complex areas reserved until Chapter 15.

CHAPTER 11

Jurassic of Inland West Dorset

The rolling hill and vale country of West Dorset involves the Lias Beds described in Chapters 2 and 3, plus patchy remains of the unconformable capping of Gault and Upper Greensand. Even on the Bridport Sand country of the Upper Lias, the area supports rich green pastureland. However, high seepages in the Lower and Middle Lias make the Vale of Marshwood an apt name. Where the Cretaceous capping survives there is sharply contrasting scenery, flat-topped hills with more steeply sloping margins, in some places wooded, in others bracken covered. The vegetation mirrors the underlying geology most effectively in winter and spring when the dead brown bracken contrasts with green Lias meadows below.

THE VALE OF MARSHWOOD

Marshwood Vale is a pericline, an elongated dome from which the beds dip outwards in all directions. The vale shows how the older beds are exposed in the centre of an eroded fold, with the apparent paradox of an upfolded feature now forming a lowland. The cause is partly the contrast between the more clayey Lower and Middle Lias and the sandy Upper Lias. Revealed in the central areas, the former are badly draining beds. They have supported destruction of their own outcrops by the Char and its tributaries. The boundaries of the vale are in the higher better-drained sands of the Upper Lias.

Concentrating on the surface appearance of the vale, notice the underlying unity with coastal exposures of the same beds. This is due to the fact that along the coast only the undercliff is worked by the sea. The middle and upper areas are eroded by subaerial agents, seepage and landslipping activity. Since these methods also play a major role inland, West Dorset has no marked contrast in landscape between its coastal and inland areas.

The solid geology revealed inland does not extend as far down the Lias succession as at the coast. There is no Blue Lias or Shales with Beef, the lowest horizon being the Lower Cement Bed of the Black Ven Marls seen in the Cards Mill Brook.

On the east, the way in which streams follow outcrops is notable, eg Marshwood Brook and the *stellare* nodule bed. The River Char in part follows this outcrop also, while Middle Brook follows the Watch Ammonite Stone horizon. Patient, detailed exploration of such stream sections is how the solid geology of the district must be studied. No doubt as downcutting proceeds the brooks will migrate laterally with the gentle easterly dips of the eastern areas, locked on to the outcrops they now follow.

The Belemnite Marls are the one group of the Lower Lias making a distinctive surface appearance in Marshwood. As on the coast, they tend to form steeper slopes with a marked flattening at

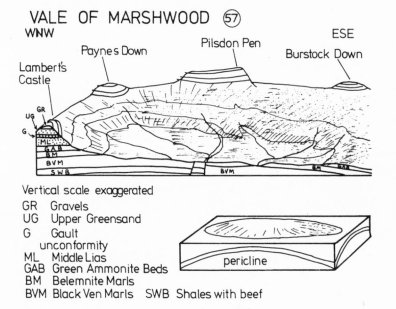

VALE OF MARSHWOOD ⑤⑦

WNW

Lambert's Castle

Paynes Down

Pilsdon Pen

ESE

Burstock Down

Vertical scale exaggerated
GR   Gravels
UG   Upper Greensand
G   Gault
     unconformity
ML   Middle Lias
GAB Green Ammonite Beds
BM   Belemnite Marls
BVM Black Ven Marls   SWB Shales with beef

pericline

the top from which the overlying Green Ammonite Beds have been eroded back. The steeper aspect prevents the Belemnite Marls being covered with debris to the same extent as the other beds. Where roads cross the Belemnite Stone horizon at their top a notch has often been cut to ease the gradient—eg south of Bluntshay Farm (414972), in Gassons Lane north of Whitchurch Canonicorum (395955). Belemnites turn up in fields above the Stone and these lands are often pitted by former marl pits.

The Green Ammonite Beds form gently sloping ground in contrast to the steeper Belemnite Marl country. Seepages occur at the Green Ammonite upper boundary with the Middle Lias and this helps to turn their sticky clay into wet land with frequent clumps of rushes.

Many of the marginal slopes of Marshwood are in rolling featureless Middle Lias. As on the coast, the base of the Starfish Bed forms a strong spring-line, and hillsides below this level are often cut by deep wooded gullies as a result. The Junction Bed at the top of the Middle Lias is missing on the west side of Marshwood. Folded into too high a position there, it was eroded away by the Cretaceous unconformity. The easterly dip soon brings it down, however, around Pilsdon Pen and Burstock Down. At both, loose blocks of it occur in hillwash and it becomes a feature farther east (see below).

On the outer margins of Marshwood, notice the difference between Gault and Upper Greensand hills which dot the ramparts of the vale and the conical-shaped hills which characterise the Bridport Sand outcrops around the Brit Valley to the east. The former, flat-topped survivors of the unconformable cover, produce the strongest outflow of springs on the west side of the vale, just as they are important primary reservoirs in the coastal landslips. Their flanks are much collapsed as a result, the springs emerging on the Gault Clay, undermining the Upper Greensand above and then slumping the latter down over the Lias beneath. The top of the Lias gradually broadens, making a marked bench at the expense of the cap rock, eg between Lambert's Castle Hill and the flanks of Payne's Down. The Gault is only rarely seen beneath the slumped hillsides. Its 9–12m of clay was a vital spring-line for village sites like Ryall and Whitchurch Canonicorum.

The strongly flat-topped character of Pilsdon Pen and Lambert's Castle is due to their good developments of Greensand Chert Beds. At the latter about 9m of Chert Beds are present, occurring in beds about 30cm thick separated by hard sandstones or siliceous glauconitic sand. Weathered cherts appear pinkish but when split reveal grey to yellowish-brown colours. The Chert Beds have been much worked for road metal on Lewesdon and Hardown Hills.

On the Dorset coast the Bridport Sands provide one of the most distinctive types of cliff (page 13). Inland their contribution is equally notable producing conical hills, eg Watton, the two Coneygars, Allington, Ryeberry, Sloes and Colmers. Most of these lie in a downfaulted tract between the Bridport and Symondsbury Faults, extending from the River Brit towards Chideock Quarry Hill. At the latter the sands are capped by the Middle Jurassic Inferior Oolite, formerly quarried there. The lane leading north from 436297 on the A35 is impassable to vehicles, which can be parked at its entrance. The lane soon enters a deep cutting in Bridport Sands. Above the slopes beyond are the overgrown quarries. Only low outcrops of the limestones are still visible, but good samples of *Ludwigia murchisonae* turn up after ploughing.

Inferior Oolite also caps Sloes and Allington Hills acting in a protective role, preserving flatter summits. Once the capping has gone, the hills degrade to the rounded conical form—despite the more calcareous sand layers, seen in the ribbed coastal cliffs. The conical-hill type is best exemplified by Colmers, with its few trees a local landmark. Note that the Down Cliff Clay, seen below the sands in their coastal exposures, is buried under hillwash inland, but old brickpits which worked it are known—North Allington at Bridport, the site of Bridport Grammar School on the east side of Coneygar Hill, Hibernia Place on the north-east of Allington Hill.

The road cutting exposure on the B3162 Bridport–Broadwindsor road at 460943 is a trap for the unwary. It lies north of the Symondsbury Fault, in Middle Lias Thorncombe Sands, also dogger filled and weathering to resemble the Bridport Sands.

THE SHELF COUNTRY

The east side of the Brit Valley is characterised by broad shelves and plateau features. These fall into two groups, both controlled by limestone beds, while the intervening slopes are of sandstone:

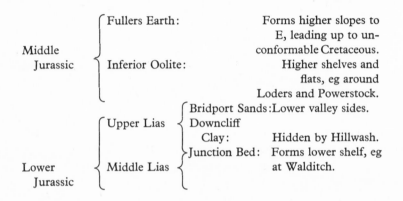

Figure 58 shows the impact of the Junction Bed shelf around Walditch. Seen from the north-east it forms an impressive flat but there are no exposures. As at its other outcrops in the district, it can be identified by its brash which turns up in the fields—astride the A3066 at Bradpole; west of Hincknoll Hill, Melplash; west of Melplash Court; at Whitecross, west of Netherbury, and around North Bowood. Since exposures are also poor in the Bridport Sands and on the Inferior Oolite upper shelf, this is a good area to practise mapping by surface features. Breaks of slope are vital evidence.

Many quarries existed in the Inferior Oolite outcrops, worked for building and limeburning, but they are all largely overgrown now. Nevertheless, some localities are still worth visiting. Richardson's papers (Bibliography) describe their former glory. The A35 around Stony Head and Loders Cross was a mecca of Inferior Oolite quarries. In 1973 road improvements created a broad cutting at Stony Head, briefly exposed but also leading to the infilling of the old Stony Head quarry. Only the Top Limestones remain visible in the four quarries around Loders

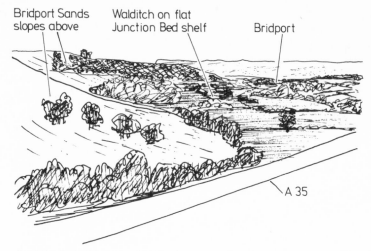

Bridport Sands slopes above — Walditch on flat Junction Bed shelf — Bridport — A 35

THE JUNCTION BED AT WALDITCH 493931 SW (58)

Cross and Vinney Cross. Their most notable features used to be the exposure of the overlying Fullers Earth at the one south of the A35 182m west of Loders Cross and the very richly fossiliferous *Astarte 'obliqua'* bed at Knights Quarry north-east of Vinney Cross.

Farther north around Mappercombe and Powerstock the shelf-like flats of the outcrop are very marked. A particularly good view is the one down the dry valley tributary of the Loders stream north-west of Mappercombe Farm. In the field corner west of the lane junction 511954 55cm of Top Limestones can be seen in the hedge, with a 7cm *Astarte 'obliqua'* bed full of *Pleurotomaria* beneath and 70cm of Red Bed below again. Noted locally for the most fossiliferous development of the beds, the old quarry at the former Powerstock Station sidings is now in the garden of a private house.

LITTON CHENEY FAULT AND SYNCLINE

Rather misleadingly, Bridport lies in the tear-faulted Brit valley while the River Bride is the lesser stream flowing from Long Bredy to the coast at Burton Bradstock. It is a small valley, yet, due to Jurassic and Cretaceous folding the post-Cretaceous faulting, there are higher beds here than any previously seen in the West Dorset Jurassic, either on the coast or inland. The Forest Marble, Cornbrash, Oxford Clay, Corallian and Kimmeridge Clay are all involved as well as the Cretaceous unconformity (Figure 59). The main faults on both margins involve Cretaceous beds which clearly dates the faults as of later age, probably Miocene.

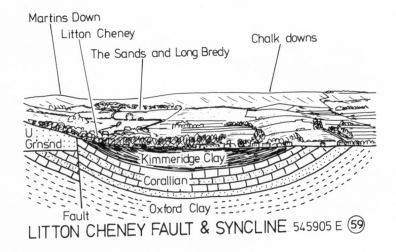

LITTON CHENEY FAULT & SYNCLINE 545905 E ⑨

CHAPTER 12

Inland Purbeck

The Isle of Purbeck is a peninsular area some 17km wide by 12km north to south. It lies south of the River Frome and east of Arish Mell Cove. The poorly drained heaths which surround the Frome and Poole Harbour at its mouth were the cause of Purbeck's isolation, giving it the reality of an island up to the late nineteenth century. The stone trade made links with the outside world, but it was sea-borne and thus never forged stronger land links with the rest of Dorset. Later, road and rail transport breached the heathlands, spurred on by the coming of tourism and rescuing Swanage just as decline set in for the stone trade.

The great chalk ridge of the Purbeck Hills seems to represent a more conscious boundary to Purbeck today. Most travellers pass through the ridge at the impressive gateway of Corfe Castle or the gap at Ulwell, but the 1:25000 map SY87/97SZ07 reveals the minor country lanes which cross the ridge. These are the way to really appreciate the Purbeck Hills, to see what those closely bunched contours mean in landscape terms.

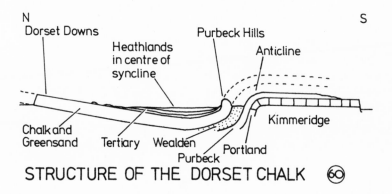

STRUCTURE OF THE DORSET CHALK

Why are the Purbeck Hills so narrow? The answer lies in the folding of the chalk beds over a much wider area of the county. The chalk is the common limb of two structures, the eroded asymmetrical Purbeck anticline to the south and the heathland covered syncline to the north.

WHITEWAYS HILL

Standing 688811 on the narrow ramparts of Purbeck first look north. Inside the army ranges the open-cast clay pit at the foot of the slopes illustrates how steeply the chalk dips north beneath the heathlands. Clear days provide distant views of it rising gently again on the far side of the syncline in the Dorset Downs.

To the south the broad vale is the Wealden outcrop crossing from Swanage Bay to Worbarrow Bay, the latter seen below at its west end. Rising from beneath the chalk, the Wealden Sands are in turn replaced by the Purbeck and Portland Beds which form the opposite slope of the valley. These beds still survive in the gentle southern limb of the Purbeck anticline and can be seen turning over to continue away as a great plateau ending at the cream-coloured cliffs of St Alban's Head in the far distance. The great plateau is the third major landscape feature of inland Purbeck. Crossing the Wealden via Steeple, make for its northern margin above Kimmeridge village and stop near 918801. The overturn of the Portland and Purbeck Beds into the northern limb of the anticline is immediately seen to be a less impressive feature than that of the chalk, but nevertheless it has many points of interest. Two old quarries by the road junction expose the Portland Stone Cherty Series. Between them a path leads up on to the flanks of Smedmore Hill, a good vantage point. The ground drops steeply everywhere below Tyneham Cap, Smedmore Hill and Swyre Head, marking the broken edge of the Portland Beds. They originally extended out from our viewpoint as part of the plateau area, but locally over Kimmeridge the plateau has been destroyed. How could the resistant stone beds be eroded away while the weaker Kimmeridge Clays survive in the lowland below? The most likely reason is that Kimmeridge Bay extended farther inland during a period of higher sea-levels. The Portland Beds were then undermined in the same fashion as Gad Cliff is today, page 134. A sea-level 55–70m higher would have sufficed. Fragments of marine-cut platforms are common at this level elsewhere in South-West England.

THE BLASHENWELL TUFA

At the south end of Corfe Castle, fork right (B3069) and cross the Wealden quartz grit and sandstones which are responsible here for Corfe Common. Figure 61 illustrates the view as the road descends the south side of the common into a tributary valley of the Corfe River. Although the steep slope ahead appears to be a scarp face it is in fact the northern dip of the Purbeck fold, here in the Purbeck Beds. The beds are repeated by a minor roll on the flank of the main fold and this causes the road to twist and turn to ease the gradient as it climbs the slope to Kingston village.

The minor roll also repeated the valuable marble bed outcrops within the Upper Purbeck Beds. Striking east and west of our route here, the north-dipping marble beds were much worked along the ridge, and quarrying hamlets existed at many spots which are now only isolated farms or barns. West Orchard, Affling-ton, Downshay, Scoles, Quarr and Wilkswood and many others were marble-working centres in the thirteenth and fourteenth centuries, strung out east along the outcrops towards Swanage (Chapter 17). Downshay was a source of marble for Salisbury Cathedral in the thirteenth century, while as late as 1800 Afflington (now only a farm) had a population of fifty.

0·8km west of the road is Blashenwell Farm. Here a remarkable tufa outcrop occurs, its origin related to the minor roll described above. Water draining west along the syncline of this minor fold built up the calcareous tufa as a land deposit about 4,500 BC, covering an area 456m by 60m and nearly 3m deep. The deposit contains remains of Mesolithic age. Over twenty species of land snails are found in it, mixed with flaked flints, animal bones and charcoal. Living here in the damp post-glacial climate, early man evidently collected limpets and periwinkles from the Purbeck

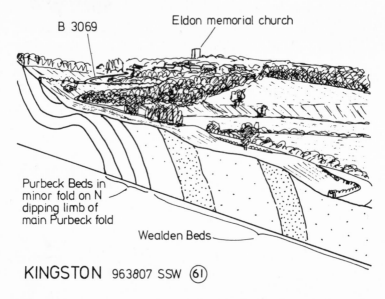

KINGSTON 963807 SSW (61)

coast and brought them inland for his food, since their marine
shells are also found in the tufa. There are several public footpaths into Blashenwell, some of them ancient marblers haulage
roads. The tufa can just be seen in a small roadside exposure
about 225m north of the farm. Unfortunately a good deal of
rubbish has been tipped into this pit recently.

KINGSTON AND WORTH MATRAVERS

Continuing up the hill to Kingston, stop at the Eldon memorial
church. It is the last great work from the local Portland and Purbeck Beds. Opened in 1880, the church had provided seven years
work for the industry. Oddly enough its building coincided with
the final decline in the trade. Some suggest it caused it, the trade
having lost its usual markets while active on the church. Doubtless
many factors were involved but, by a twist of fate, a fine memorial
to the industry now stands in a village which itself was never a
very active quarrying centre, even in the thirteenth century. The
marble industry is described in Chapter 17, but the luxury nature
of its use, only for the finest interior work, can be readily appre-

ciated in the superb polished columns of this church. Myriad shells of the tiny pond snail *Viviparus* crowd the slabs of fresh-water limestone. A point worth remembering is that the marble beds are thin—high columns could only be achieved by mounting long slabs on end.

A choice of routes is available to those wishing to reach the coast at Chapman's Pool. There is the toll road along the east side of the churchyard, or via Worth Matravers another leads down past Renscombe Farm and Hill Bottom. Alternatively, walk east to Afflington Barn and then down the footpath to Coombe and Hill Bottoms. The latter routes pass close to Swanworth Quarry, about 1·6km north of Worth Matravers. The quarry face extends in levels from the Cherty Series up to the Lower Purbeck Beds. What is visible at each level depends on the current state of quarrying operations. Generally the Cherty Series is seen in the lowest face, the Freestones largely on the middle shelf, with the Shrimp Bed outcropping at eye level on the upper shelf and Lower Purbeck Beds occupying the rest of the face above it.

Worth Matravers must be the most attractive village in Purbeck. Nothing blends better with a landscape than its own natural stone. The cottages are roofed with stone-slates from the thinner beds. The village forms the centre for a fine circular walk to Houn-stout, St Alban's Head and Winspit—if you can tear yourself away from its charms (Chapter 5). The 1:25000 map is the ideal guide. If a level walk is desired try the route south to St Alban's Head. This passes the small St Alban's Quarry, in the Portland Stone Beds.

SWANAGE QUARRIES

In the Swanage district there are three types of quarry—all of them the practical result of the disposition of the beds (Figure 60). To the south valuable stone horizons in the cliffs were worked by galleries while, on the plateau above, open pits were sunk and then worked laterally, backfilling with the waste stone. In the steep north limb of the anticline, however, roughly along a line running west from Swanage, much of the working was by inclined mine shafts, following the dip underground. There are no active stone mines left (Chapter 17), only the plateau-top open quarries are active today. Their sites have changed over the years, of course, but only slowly. It is surprising how long it takes to exhaust all the usable horizons of quite small areas. The clearance of a new working area is a relatively infrequent event. The quarries look a little chaotic, but this is because higher beds from the new area have to be stripped off and stockpiled for later use, thus enabling lower beds to be worked direct from the pit at the same time.

The open quarries are grouped in two east-west belts, due to the effect of the east-west Zig-Zag Path fault in Durlston Bay (page 98). An older belt of abandoned quarries runs along the top of the southerly coastal slopes. Walking north towards Swanage, the dip carries the beds deeper until the course of the fault is reached, when they are brought up again to recommence the process. The second belt of quarries takes advantage of this feature and occupies the crest-line of the high ground south of Swanage, Langton Matravers and Acton. Some present-day workings are also on the plateau top between the two belts.

Quarries sometimes break into old stone mine galleries. Enormous advances in earth-moving machinery since the mid twentieth century were not available to the old Purbeck stone miners, so even up on the plateau they would choose to mine rather than hand-dig vast amounts of overburden. Another point to remember is that Purbeck Bed material is very variable. A good roof level was essential and many parts had to be cut to waste to get at the more valuable stone. Variation in thickness means that all the quarries produce a variety of items, from large walling stones to brick or random sized house building material and very thin slabs for crazy paving or roofing.

The principal workings now are at Acton, at Paine's California Farm quarry and at Suttle's Pit a few hundred metres east again. Paine's Quarry (018775) was opened about fourteen years ago. The main face is working north but because of the numerous usable beds it is surprising how small an area has been worked to date. A set of casts of dinosaur footprints discovered here a few years ago can be seen in the drive of Periwinkles Cottage, Cotness,

922832. In the caravan park north of the quarry there are remains of old stone mines (Chapter 17). Suttle's Pits, a little to the east, have moved south to their present site, having formerly worked the Swanage Quarries of the northern belt at 022780, now the Swanage rubbish tip. Surviving sections can still be examined around its margins. Use the 1:25000 map for rights of way through the quarrying grounds.

PURBECK DINOSAURS

The Purbeck Beds yield remains of turtles, crocodiles and dinosaurs, among other reptiles. With the ichthyosaurs and plesiosaurs of the Kimmeridge Clay, Oxford Clay and Lower Lias beds, they make Dorset the premier English county for the study of reptilian fossils. At least 103 named forms are known in Dorset, forty-three of these genera and species apparently unique to the county. The Purbeck Beds particularly contain forms which are unique or rare elsewhere.

Dinosaurs are divided into two orders: those with a reptilian bone arrangement of the pelvis (Saurischia) and those with bird-like arrangements of it (Ornithischia). The two dinosaurs most frequently found in Dorset come by chance one from each group. The first order subdivides as follows:

Saurischia ⎰ Sauropoda (herbivorous and amphibious)
⎱ Theropoda (carnivorous) ⎰ Coelurosauria
⎱ Carnosauria -inc *Megalosaurus*

Megalosaurus is the Dorset representative of the Carnosauria. They had large skulls, large sharp recurved teeth, small degenerate forelimbs, tails used for balancing, powerful hind limbs and thinner more well-defined toes on their three-toed feet—perhaps for agility in hunting their prey. The first dinosaur described was a *Megalosaurus* specimen (Buckland, 1824). The other most common Dorset dinosaur is *Iguanodon* from the Ornithischia. Also walking on its hind legs and about 9m long, *Iguanodon* was herbivorous. It had a long beak instead of front teeth, the rest of its teeth being adapted to crushing vegetable food.

The remarkable feature of the Purbeck Beds are the plentiful footprints but few remains of any species skeletons in the formation. Equally amazing—the multitude of crocodilian reptiles apparently left no prints at all! This is the fact that anyone attracted to the study of reptile remains in Purbeck must face—the main finds are footprints, ie trace fossils. In recent years prints have been discovered in local quarries in 1932, 1961, 1963, 1965, 1967 (2 sets). Irrespective of the species involved, the prints have usually been about 25cm in diameter with a pace of about 1m. The shortest track uncovered was of eight prints, the longest of sixteen. In all

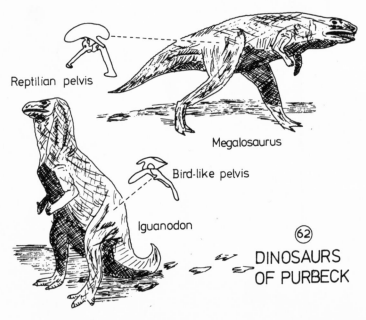

Reptilian pelvis

Megalosaurus

Bird-like pelvis

Iguanodon

62 DINOSAURS
OF PURBECK

tracks the alternate prints point slightly inward, indicating a swinging gait or that the creatures were pigeon-toed.

Most of the footprints discovered in Purbeck occur in the Purbeck Roach Bed, a shelly limestone in the middle of the Freestone Vein of the Upper Building Stones. Like the Purbeck clay mines,

Purbeck quarrymen call the usable beds 'veins' (page 204). There is no sign of squelching and displacement of sediment around the footprints. Squeezing and bulging would have been inevitable in sands and clays or in limestones already filled with a good lime mud matrix. The shelly Roach, however, behaved like snow, absorbing the load by the crushing of the shells. The prints are seldom more than 10cm deep, but the sediment may be distorted for another 15cm below that again. Sometimes, where the filling has been hard to remove, it has proved difficult to tell which layer was the actual base of the print—it could even have been a higher bed, quickly eroded away again afterwards, all the 'prints' really being the distorted under-layers.

The nature of the Roach bed may also explain the sizes discovered. Below a certain weight the crunching effect would not occur, so only the larger animals left prints—hence the absence of any crocodile or turtle tracks. Remember, when examining the material at Cotness referred to above, that those are casts, material filling the prints and still adhering to the underside of the succeeding bed.

Why then are there so many prints yet so few skeletal remains in Purbeck? Although most prints came from the Roach, discoveries in other horizons show that many generations of dinosaurs must be involved. Yet, even in the Dirt Beds where other remains have been found, there are no skeletons of *Megalosaurus* or *Iguanodon*. Evidently the carnivorous *Megalosaurus* did not eat *Iguanodon* or there would have been plenty of the latter's remains. No doubt both species were living and dying elsewhere. Their prints must represent occasional forays across the Purbeck flats—*Megalosaurus* finding plenty of crocodile and turtle, *Iguanodon* perhaps enjoying seaweed and pondweed. In addition to local museums, Purbeck dinosaur tracks are housed in the British Museum (Natural History), Glasgow and Edinburgh Museums.

CHAPTER 13

The South Dorset Chalk Downs

The chalk downs form a great curving outcrop through Dorset, the north and south limbs of the syncline cradling the heathlands (Figure 60). As the diagram shows, the limbs of the syncline have very different dips and hence the two outcrops are quite different in character—the southern one a narrow, vertically bedded rampart, the Purbeck Hills, while the northern one (mainly outside the scope of this book) is a more typical scarp and vale downland landscape. Contrasting with the varied Jurassic sandstone, limestone and clay landscapes to the west and south, the chalk downlands form a buffer between them and the Tertiary heathlands.

The great contrast of the downlands is partly due to their geological unconformity, but it is accentuated because chalk creates such distinctive scenery. Its porous nature results in dry valleys and underground drainage—thus protecting surface areas from erosion and creating upland country. All these features combine to affect vegetation, settlement and land-use. Nowhere is this more evident than in the steep southern limb.

THE PURBECK HILLS

Without doubt the finest views in Purbeck are obtained by walking along the commanding ridge of upturned chalk, the Purbeck Hills. Starting from the road above Ulwell or from Whiteways Hill in the west, you can divide the hills into two sections and have a downhill finish at Corfe Castle on each. For convenience here, the hills are described in east-west order.

North-west of Swanage the hills are very nearly breached by a second gap, the Ulwell Valley, which is cut along a fault. The gap is followed by the Swanage–Studland road which otherwise would have had to zigzag over the ridge like the lane between Church Knowle and East Creech.

Numerous chalk pits have been opened from time to time along the Purbeck Hills. None is large and many older ones have almost vanished without trace. The intense deformation of the steeply dipping chalk has crushed fossil specimens and, since the zones are poorly endowed locally anyway, collecting in the pits is an often unrewarding task. Unfortunately the vanished pits were the most fossiliferous. The large pit in the Ullwell Gap at 018811 is thought to be in the *cortestudinarium* zone while another west of the lane up to Currendon Farm must be in a higher zone, but is very shattered and crystalline, lying close to the downthrow side of the Ulwell Fault.

Westwards along the hills there are two more pits which are relatively well exposed: at 986820 by the bridleways to Brenscombe Hill one which is probably in the *cortestudinarium* zone again, and a *mucronata* zone pit at 970824 south of Rollington Farm. The café and car park north of Corfe Castle lie in another probable *mucronata* pit, while west of the castle on the flanks of West Hill a longer section is revealed from *plenus* Marl to near the top of the *planus* zone, 956822. Leaving the other interests of Corfe Castle for the moment, the remaining pits are concentrated in the Church Knowle-Creechbarrow area.

Above Cocknowle the chalk was worked for cement. The now overgrown scar along the hillside above the lane exposed *labiatus* zone chalk. A short distance farther up the lane, a path providing a short cut northwards now follows the track of an old cable-hauled inclined railway over into the valley below Stonehill Down. The cement then went on by cart across the heaths to Ridge on the Wareham Channel. The little dry valley on the north of the hills here is the only strike valley cut into the Purbeck Hills. The large quarry cut into its northern slopes below Stonehill Down is frustratingly well exposed but poorly fossiliferous, 931823.

A few remaining patches of *mucronata* chalk are visible at the col south of Creechbarrow where the stone was used in limekilns, but fossiliferous sites around Whiteway Hill are regrettably inside the army ranges. Almost everywhere along the foot of the Purbeck Hills there are hollows where local farmers have dug the decayed surface chalk for use on the fields as marl, eg along the south side eastwards from Corfe Castle.

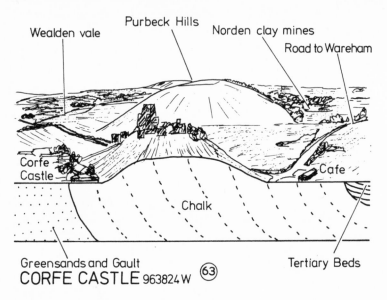

CORFE CASTLE 963824 W (63)

CORFE CASTLE

Few castles can occupy a more splendid site commanding a natural lowland gateway than Corfe Castle, dating from Norman times and sitting on a knoll over 45m high. This seemingly man-made mound is in fact a natural accident, being left between the Corfe River and the Byle Brook. How did these streams succeed in breaching the ramparts of the Purbeck Hills to cross the heaths to Poole Harbour? As with so many geological posers, the answer lies in being able to visualise the time scale and the gradual development to the present situation. These brooks rose on the chalk cover when it continued over to the south. Removal of the crest then proceeded to reveal the Wealden outcrop whose surface was then roughly at the same height as the remaining chalk of the Purbeck Hills. Uniting then, as they do today, just north of the chalk outcrop, the two streams began to lower themselves into it.

The chalk is hard here, so it was not widened easily. In more recent times it has been worked locally as road metal. Gorges resulted and as the gaps were lowered leaving the castle knoll between them, so the Wealden vale to the south was lowered to the new levels. Erosion of the Wealden was directly controlled by the speed of the deepening at Corfe Castle. All this took place before the coastal erosion at the west and east ends of the Wealden vale had developed the present Worbarrow and Swanage Bays. Now that these shorter routes to the sea exist, it is possible that their streams will enlarge their drainage at the expense of the central system. Details of Corfe Castle's association with the Purbeck marble trade are given in Chapter 17.

DOWNLAND DRY VALLEYS

As noted earlier, few of the dry valleys so typical of chalk downland are found in the Purbeck Hills. However, they become a feature to the west and, as in central and northern Dorset, are formed during the erosion of the porous chalk landscapes. As the chalk scarps have retreated in Dorset so the level of the Upper Greensand and Gault outcrops at their base has been lowered— and these are the outcrops which, with their important spring-lines, play a major part in controlling the level of the water-table under neighbouring downlands. As the spring-line on the scarp areas is lowered, so the springs feeding the valleys over on the dip-slope are forced to issue at lower and lower levels. The heads of combes are soon left above outflow level and, as scarp recession continues, the dry valley sections on the downland above grow longer.

Chaldon Down, the first broad area of downland west of the Purbeck Hills, is unvaried chalk country with dry valleys. One of the very few exposures of its Upper Chalk is seen along the Winfrith Newburgh–East Lulworth road, 813820. The Greensand is too far below to make any contribution to valley development. It appears to the south in coastal sections already described and also to the north where it comes up in a periclinal structure at Chaldon Herring (Chapter 16).

To the west, leave the A353 at Upton and visit Spring Bottom Ridge, described in Chapter 9. This Cretaceous syncline, perched in a now upland position on the south side of an earlier Jurassic syncline, is the first area going west where the Upper Greensand plays its customary role in feeding out water at the base of the slopes. The footpath south from Upton through the grounds of Spring Bottom House passes close to the springs which are the origin of the name.

BINCOMBE DOWN

One of the most obvious and best-known inland chalk pits is at the junction of the Broadmayne Lane with the A354, 672859, north-west of Bincombe Down. In flinty Upper Chalk, it is worth photographing for the buried soil layer near its top. The pit is in the *Marsupites* zone, soft chalk dipping 10° north and yielding plates of the sea-urchin *Marsupites testudinarius,* as well as sponges *Porosphaera globularis* and *Porosphaera nuciformis* which look rather like little round oak apples.

COMPTON VALENCE DOME NW ⑥④

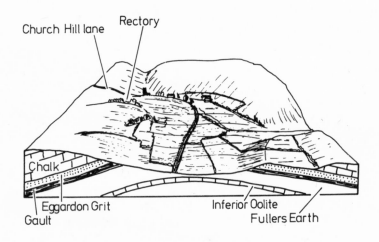

Church Hill lane   Rectory

Chalk

Eggardon Grit
Gault

Inferior Oolite
Fullers Earth

THE COMPTON VALENCE DOME

This interesting little structure forms a window through the downlands into the basement below. Unconformable Chalk, Upper Greensand and Gault have all been eroded away from the summit of a fold in Jurassic Fullers Earth Beds—rather like exposing a buried hilltop. The structure can be viewed from several points on the road along its south side. It lies on an anticlinal axis running east from Pilsdon Pen (Vale of Marshwood) through Eggardon Hill. The Eggardon Grit (see below) is exposed around the dome, dipping outwards up to 25° in every direction. It can be seen on the western slopes and forms a cliff below the Rectory, 591932, with a good spring issuing from its base. Sloping ledges of it can be traced on the north-east and south-west margins. Note the drainage of the dome north-east to the Frome Valley—the catchment and spring supply is not yet enough to deepen the valley sufficiently and ensure a permanent flow. The stream is absorbed into the chalk at 604932.

EGGARDON HILL

Eggardon Hill, 542946, is the finest viewpoint at the western margin of the Dorset Downs. 243m high, it crowns the margins of the Brit Valley drainage. From below its unconformity long slopes of Fullers Earth drop west to the shelf country around Uploders and Powerstock described in Chapter 11. Notice how the broad valleys of the nearer slopes suddenly narrow as they reach those areas. They have cut vertically through the shelves, but the Inferior Oolite capping has clearly restricted valley widening. Beyond, the distinctive conical-hilled Bridport Sand country can be seen and the highest skylines to the west are the detached remnants of the Cretaceous cover at Golden Cap etc. Imagine these rocks as they once were, a continuous cover stretching across to the ground beneath you on Eggardon Hill. To the south there are more outliers visible, Shipton and Hammiton Hills.

A hill fort occupies the broadest part of the long spur of Eggardon Hill. From its south-west ramparts at 358947 the Eggardon

EGGARDON HILL ⑥⑤

Brit valley

Jurassic bedded lower ground
with shelves of
Inferior Oolite

Eggardon Grit outcrop

537946 N

Grit beds

Exogyra sandstones

536953 SW

Grit capped slipped mass

Grit can be seen outcropping along the south-west slopes, a local
development at the top of the Upper Greensand. Near the Bell
Stone at the end of the spur several small scars expose the grit and
other parts of the Upper Greensand succession beneath it. The
end of the hill is in two levels, the higher one exposing the grit
which really consists of three beds. The upper 2m is the hard
layer, a yellow and green quartz grit with glauconite. It weathers
in a rough honeycombed way and slightly overhangs the other
two beds which are 20cm of coarse quartz with *Holaster* and
Exogyra and about 1m of nodular quartz sand.

The succession can be continued on the lower or outer part of
the spur, down into the Chert Beds and Exogyra Sandstone. The
Chert Beds are not well developed here. Consisting mainly of
sands, they are rather overgrown. In the underlying sandstones
the number of *Exogyra* varies enormously, being most numerous
0·3–1m and 2–3·5m from the top. Just below the exposures the
hillside is broken by what appears to be a second grit bed, the top
of a landslipped mass. A careful check of its top surface reveals a
dip towards the hill, caused by tilting during the slumping.

CHAPTER 14

The Heathlands

Cradled in a great syncline of chalk, the Tertiary heathlands are the heartland of Dorset. It is a heartland of great contrasts— barren wastes of crunchy gravel covered with blooming gorse and heathland plants on the one hand, ribbons of rich silt-fed meadows along the Frome and Stour rivers on the other. But the bulk of the area belongs to the first type of landscape. Useless agriculturally in the past, it barely provided subsistence for the poor heath-cropping families who were its only inhabitants. A moody land-scape, hot and stifling in summer, bleak cold and brooding in winter, it was a place in which a tolerable income could be won from the clays and gravels beneath its surface rather than from what grew upon it. To the heath came, and still come, the sand and gravel men, the clay diggers and miners. Their visual impact on the heath is small, however, despite its more fragmentary modern extent. What seemed to Hardy's generation a wild and fearful place is still sizeable enough to act as an oasis of peace and solitude in the modern world. Go up to the Agglestone or away across the old gravel workings around Moreton, and Hardy's words are as valid as ever: 'the eye could reach nothing of the world outside the summits and shoulders of the heathland which filled the whole circumference of its glance, and to know that everything around and underneath had been from prehistoric times as unaltered as the stars overhead gave ballast to the mind adrift on change' (*The Return of the Native*, Macmillan)

The sand and gravel shoulders hide the other element of heath-land geology, the lenses of clays which give apparently dry ground a surprisingly high water-table, quickly waterlogging the surface in wet weather. Runs of unconsolidated sands also contribute to the hummocky look of the area. The Reading Beds and London

Clay have been described at Studland Cliffs (page 101) and above them come the Bagshot Beds, containing the important Pipe Clay Series.

THE PIPECLAY SERIES

Do not be misled by the name for in addition to the lenses of fine clays, several metres thick when they are well developed, these beds are predominantly quartz sands with sandy clays, shaly and carbonaceous clays and occasional thin bands of ironstone. The quartz sands are typical Bagshot Sands and, like the other types of deposit, were laid down in the vast river delta which covered the area in Eocene times. The river flowed eastwards carrying large quantities of material in suspension. The coarser materials formed sandy deposits where the velocity of flow was checked, the finer being deposited as seams of clay in the quieter backwaters. The banks and inlets were overhung by rich plant growth. Insects wing cases found in the deposits serve to remind the student of the similar conditions of Purbeck times.

Pipeclay and ball clay are synonymous, the former arising because clay-pipe making was a major use of the material at one time, the latter a reference to the old method of working it. The important geological feature is that the deposits were transported and naturally sorted. Comparable deposits exist in Devon near Petrockstow and in the Bovey Basin (see *Geology Explained in South and East Devon*, Chapter 12). In contrast the china clays of the south-west granite districts are residual clays—decomposed but still at their original site. China clays must be washed to separate the quartz and clay material (*Geology Explained: Dartmoor & Tamar Valley*, Chapters 2, 7). The old idea is that ball clays were derived by river transport from the residual china clays. More recently weathering of Culm Measures has been suggested as a source, in which case the material may still have come from SW England and been mixed with the sandier stuff on the way. The origin has still to be proved.

Figure 67 shows the variations in the Pipe Clay Series built up through the delta. Sequences from the various boreholes indicated would differ widely. Today sections in ball clay can only be seen in active open pits or in underground mines. The colourful heathland plants quickly reclaim abandoned open workings. If permission to visit is not obtained, faces can be seen from the roadside at Norden, north of Corfe Castle, 953826, New Barn Pit at East Holme, 895853; and with binoculars the large pit inside the army ranges at Povington can be viewed from West Creech Hill, 894815. The clay is varied in colour, grey, white or mottled red, but an important feature is its freedom from impurities. The material fires white, creamy white or buff and is refractory. In ceramics it provides good bonding, strength and increased plasticity in working and moulding, and strength in the fired product. Its greater plasticity compared to china clays is due to the finer particle size of these transported or derived deposits. Ball clay is a valuable ingredient in the manufacture of a wide range of goods including domestic tableware, sanitary ware, electrical insulators, glazed tiles, fire cements and crucibles. A typical Dorset ball clay contains in percentages:

Silica dioxide SiO_2 (Quartz)	52	Magnesium oxide MgO	0·5
Titanium dioxide TiO_2	0·9	Calcium oxide CaO	0·3
Aluminium oxide Al_2O_3	31	Potassium oxide K_2O	3·1
Iron oxide Fe_2O_3	1·4	Sodium oxide Na_2O	0·4

THE BALL CLAY INDUSTRY TODAY

An early member of the Pike family described the clayworks as 'an uneventful industry in an uneventful place'. The timeless spirit of the heath was evidently in his blood. The modern traveller may well feel the same. Except for the openworks around Norden, where is this modern industry? How can it produce over 100,000 tonnes of clay per year here and yet be so inconspicuous? The answer is in its selective nature—quality rather than quantity, selection rather than bulk. The industry thus blends into, even hides amidst, the varied landscapes of an area which embraces high open views from the Purbeck Hills, the small landscapes of Hardy's shoulders and summits, and the water landscape of Poole Harbour.

THE BALL CLAY INDUSTRY

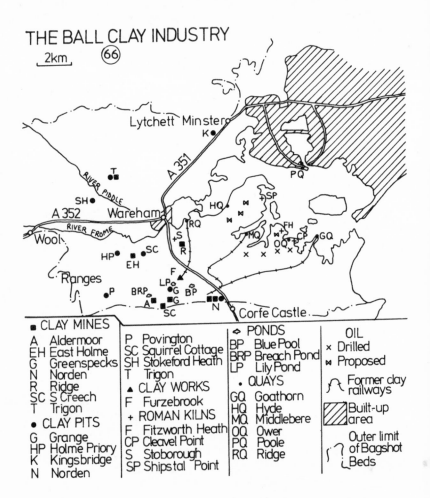

2km (66)

■ CLAY MINES		◇ PONDS	OIL
A Aldermoor	P Povington	BP Blue Pool	× Drilled
EH East Holme	SC Squirrel Cottage	BRP Breach Pond	⋈ Proposed
G Greenspecks	SH Stokeford Heath	LP Lily Pond	
N Norden	T Trigon	• QUAYS	⌢ Former clay railways
R Ridge	▲ CLAY WORKS		
SC S Creech	F Furzebrook	GQ Goathorn	
T Trigon	+ ROMAN KILNS	HQ Hyde	▨ Built-up area
• CLAY PITS	F Fitzworth Heath	MQ Middlebere	
G Grange	CP Cleavel Point	OQ Ower	⌒ Outer limit of Bagshot Beds
HP Holme Priory	S Stoborough	PQ Poole	
K Kingsbridge	SP Shipstal Point	RQ Ridge	
N Norden			

Formerly most of the clay was obtained from open pits. The labourers worked them in steps marking out the surface of each level in squares, using the special spade or tubal from which ball clay is said to be named, then spiking and lifting out the 'balls'. Seventy balls made a mines ton of 22½ cwt. One early use of the clay was to burn it and dust it on roads—small wonder that water transport was more important then! As far as the early pottery industry went, the clayworks only dug, graded, turned and

SECTION IN THE BALL CLAY DEPOSITS ⑥⑦

Emphasising the variable borehole results and small proportion of fine clays

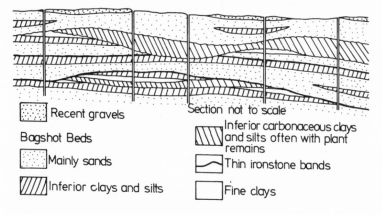

Recent gravels

Bagshot Beds

Mainly sands

Inferior clays and silts

Section not to scale

Inferior carbonaceous clays and silts often with plant remains

Thin ironstone bands

Fine clays

weathered the clay, the potters experimenting with its firing properties.

Open pits can encounter up to three times as much overburden as there is clay. The pits are generally partly backfilled and some beautiful ponds of high amenity value have resulted. Blue Pool is a commercialised example; others (Figure 66) are encircled by trees and full of fish and water birds.

Today, ball clays are worked by open pit and underground mining methods. The clay company is the quality controller now, offering the potter fifteen or more grades, ready blended with particular ceramic properties. The mines work high quality clay only. A clay mine has an expected life at of least fifteen years. For conservation purposes its surface buildings are demountable for removal after working out. Mines vary greatly in size—a reflection of the variable underground geology. Workable clay seams are usually 2m thick, and must be covered by at least 5m of impervious strata to protect the workings from influxes of water from sandy beds overhead. Only in more complex areas such as Norden is there more than one workable horizon per mine. Here the upper bed is worked first, then controlled subsidence allowed to take place before working the lower one. Dorset clay miners often refer to the beds as veins—a term geologists reserve for metallic mineral deposits. There are two mines at Norden, one a vertical shaft, the other the more usual adit type. Their beds correlate with those of another shaft mine at Ridge, near Stoborough, but the correlation is lost in between. Topographically and stratigraphically higher are the clay beds of Creechbarrow, now the deepest workings in the Dorset clay field. The three mines there produce clays from the same seam. The mines which can be seen easily without permission to actually enter are Ridge 932855 and South Creech 922822. All the clays are taken to the shredding and blending works at Furzebrook—another feature which explains the small surface area required at the mines themselves. The end products are the famous Dorset ball clays, firing ivory in colour, and stronger and more plastic than their white-firing South Devon counterparts.

Early exploration was on a wildcat basis and the pits were concentrated in limited areas, eg Norden. These districts still produce good clay but drilling is now systematic, filling many previous gaps in knowledge of the deposits. The industry keeps 20–30 years' reserves in sight, and this has inevitably focussed its interest on controversial areas such as the Arne Peninsula, famous for its bird reserves and particularly its colony of Dartford warblers.

Dorset ball clay is exported to Europe and many other countries, but the area is more home-market orientated than South Devon. The clay is sent by road and rail. The export port, controlled by the ship and destination nowadays, may be as far away as Par in Cornwall. For adit methods etc, see *Geology Explained in South and East Devon* (Chapter 12).

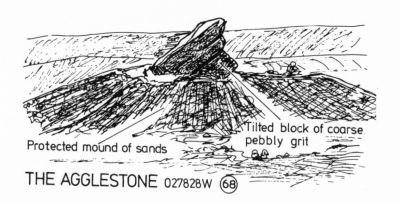

Tilted block of coarse pebbly grit

Protected mound of sands

THE AGGLESTONE 027828W (68)

THE AGGLESTONE

At the top of the Bagshot Beds, the Agglestone Grit takes its name from the conspicuous rock sitting on the heaths about 0·8km NNW of the village. How similar to the Wealden ironstones the rock looks at close quarters (Figure 68). The block is estimated to weigh 500 tonnes. It is slightly less commanding now than it was, since it slipped a bit sideways in 1970, no doubt an adjustment to the slow removal of sand beneath. Another smaller example, the Puckstone, lies to the north-west. Many smaller blocks are scattered over the heaths or appear locally in house or garden walls. They form what are known as puddingstone.

CREECHBARROW

Described geologically as 'the most noteworthy hill composed of Tertiary Beds in England', Creechbarrow remains unnamed on OS maps, its summit at 922824. Ringed to east, north and west by old claypit ponds, it is not surprising that mines follow the clay beds beneath the hill itself and three in fact surround it (Figure 66). They originally met beneath the hill but have since separated again as extraction retreats towards the entrances. Aldermoor, below the north-west slopes, has the largest output of any Dorset clay mine, over 15,000 tonnes per year. Make for the col south of the hill where South Creech Mine stands. Worked now for over twenty years, the mine access plunges north at a 1 in 3 gradient. A path to the summit begins near the mine, leading to one of the most expansive views in Dorset. At 193m, the top of Creechbarrow surpasses parts of the Purbeck Hills chalk ridge, and to the south-east the Wealden vale beyond Corfe is visible. Figure 69 shows the geology of the hill which is notable since the Eocene beds have been upturned against the chalk ridge here, positive proof of Tertiary fold activity in Dorset.

Buildings have existed on the hill, so its flat top is man made. The summit's different geology is reflected in its grass cover—no gorse or heath plants. There are no rock exposures either. Knowledge of the beds involved was obtained by specially dug pits. The summit area does in fact contain a limestone—the Creechbarrow Limestone—at first believed to be Oligocene in age which would make it a higher part of the Tertiary succession than anything seen on the heaths below. Recent studies suggest it may be Eocene, however.

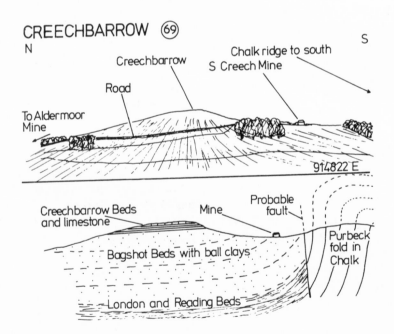

CREECHBARROW ⑥⑨

Creechbarrow Limestone, porous and tufaceous	2–3m		Eocene or Oligocene?
Sands with bands of flints	6–9m	Creechbarrow	
Buff brick clay, flints at base	18m	Beds	Eocene
Sand and coarse grit			

If the Creechbarrow Limestone is Oligocene it could be related to the Bembridge Limestone of the Isle of Wight. Fresh, little rolled flints found in the other Creechbarrow Beds indicate that the chalk immediately to the south was being eroded before the limestone was deposited. The Purbeck fold was already active, but its creation lasted long enough to affect the attitude of the Tertiary Beds as well.

DORSET BRICKMAKING

Dorset has abundant sand, gravel and clay deposits in its Jurassic and Tertiary strata. A map of known sites where clays have been worked, whatever the purpose—bricks, pottery, pipes etc—reveals a generally even density of sites, the only gaps being along the outcrop of the chalk downs. In the heaths north of Poole Harbour the map goes haywire with thick clusters of sites. Now nearly all disused, they have in many cases disappeared under the urban growth of Poole and Bournemouth—the very expansion that created a demand for their products.

Clays are rocks with particles less than 1/256mm in size which have an ability to lose or take up moisture according to temperature and the amount available. When wet they become plastic; when dry they shrink and crack. The amount of shrinkage is crucial in brick and pottery manufacture—clays are unmanageable if it exceeds 30 per cent and preliminary drying is usually necessary anyway. The drying must remove sufficient water. What remains trapped can then combine chemically with alumina, silica, iron, etc in the clays and form a silicate glass. A well-fired product has just enough of this glass to bond any unfused particles together. Another important item is the minor chemical material present. Soda lime and magnesium help the fluxing, but excess of them can cause over-vitrification. Most Jurassic clays contain organic carbon, sulphur and bituminous material. The first two give the unweathered clays their blue-grey colour (Chickerell pits, page 51) while the latter assists firing and saves fuel. Such clays require exact firing. All the remaining water must be driven off or chemically combined before the carbon will burn, and in turn the latter must be burnt before the iron sulphides present will oxidise and turn the blue-grey clay into red-coloured bricks. Problems arise if there is more alumina, silica and iron than the amount needed for fluxing, for once the steam and carbon have gone, surpluses then combine with the sulphur, forming unsightly white sulphate crusts on exposed brick faces. Releasing water on heating in sunlight and taking it up again on cooling, the sulphates may eventually disintegrate the brickwork.

The earliest use of brick in Dorset buildings was in the late sixteenth century. For another 100 years bricks were always made as near the building operations as possible, usually within 16km of the site, a feature partly explaining the proliferation of pits. Units were small, often worked by one or two men. Digging was a winter occupation with hand-moulding in summer (700–800 per man day) and the kiln was fired whenever enough were ready, perhaps once a month. In these early sites the yards were surprisingly compact—no one wanted to carry heavy clay! Only in the more commercial mid-nineteenth century pits did the clay face eventually become remote from the kiln and perhaps require a small tramway.

Brickmaking received a fillip with the repeal of a tax on bricks in 1850, the coming of the railways in that decade, town growth and increasing appreciation of the architectural potential of brick. It was used with stone cornices; patterns and textures were created by careful arrangement of the various courses of stretchers (face visible) and headers (end visible). Experiments were made with different colours. Hardly a building was put up without a decorative area of glazed tiling somewhere, or a terracotta frieze, panel, lintel or chimney pot. The expansion also attracted products by rail from major production areas outside the county, eg Bridgwater, where twenty companies were active.

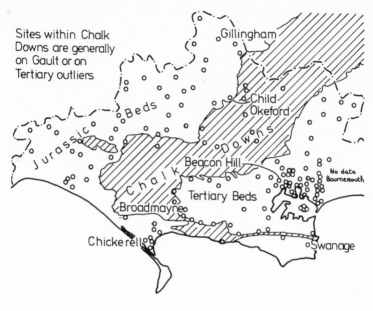

Sites within Chalk
Downs are generally
on Gault or on
Tertiary outliers

Gillingham

Child
Okeford

Beds

Jurassic

Downs

Beacon Hill

Chalk

No data
Bournemouth

Broadmayne

Tertiary Beds

Chickerell

Swanage

DORSET BRICKWORKS ⑳   After Young

Use of such sources, combined with the local products, has
given Dorset a rich variety of brick colours. Towns, buildings,
even entire suburbs, can be linked directly with changing fashions
in colours, activity of local yards, or the favouring of some distant
source. For example, the drab browns of much of Dorchester are
the local Broadmayne products (see below). The Fordington area
of the town, built 1860–90, is almost all of this brick, the whites or
yellows used for relief being probably from Poole. Eighteenth-
century parts of Weymouth are similar, but later on Weymouth
building was dominated by the harsher reds and oranges of
Chickerell. As well as their local products, Bridport and Poole
contain bricks from a wide area, since large parts of both towns
were built after the coming of the railway when imported Stafford-
shire and Berkshire bricks were as fashionable as Bridgwater's.

In brickyards, the greater demand resulted in scaling up the
operations by two additions: an automatic extrusion and wire-
cutting machine and, in large concerns, a continuous burning kiln.

Thus outputs of 1,000 bricks per man day were possible, although the products were regarded as inferior to hand-made and only used in utility work. Local products still dominated areas away from the railway lines, but road transport soon increased to 40km the 16km radius served by horse and cart.

North of Poole Harbour, brickmaking concentrated on those parts of the Bagshot Beds clays unsuitable for pottery. The greater proportion of quartz in the deposits allowed the production of durable, heavy-duty stoneware goods, such as salt-glaze sanitary ware and sewer pipes.

Apart from urban growth, the Dorset clay trades also served agriculture, manufacturing porous earthenware pipes for field drainage. Eighteenth-century field drains had been constructed of brushwood, then came the arch-shaped brick and finally the porous pipe.

At Beacon Hill, 976947, quartz sands are dug and blended with similar material from elsewhere to make modern calc-silica bricks in steam kilns. Colour is obtained by additives, however, although it is similar to the range caused by position in the kiln, eg Swanage, page 93. The golden colour of the huge Bagshot Sand quarry at the works is a prominent landmark from many parts of Poole Harbour. On the north-west of the pit are fine examples of frost-heaved structures in surface deposits.

THE WESTERN HEATHLANDS

A major sand and gravel working area occurs around Moreton and Warmwell, once again based on the variable Bagshot Beds (Figure 71). These pits reveal the beds at the west end of the heaths where they overstep other Tertiary beds beneath (the London Clay and Reading Beds). Farther west, the Bagshot Beds rest directly on the chalk itself (see below). Useful sections are preserved in some of the old pits where they abut on to railway lines or roads. Gradually obscured by rainwash they should nevertheless outlive any sections within the workings. One example bounds Redbridge Lane, Moreton Heath, running from 776878 to 784884. Travel along the lane and it appears to be a normal hedge-bordered

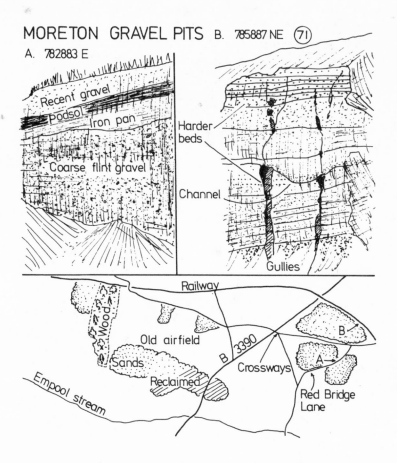

MORETON GRAVEL PITS B. 785887 NE ⑦

A. 782883 E

Recent gravel

Podsol

Iron pan

Coarse flint gravel

Harder beds

Channel

Gullies

Railway

Wood

Old airfield

Sands

Empool stream

Reclaimed

B 3390

Crossways

B

A

Red Bridge Lane

country lane. A look over the hedge reveals that the road is now 6m above pits on either side, an elevated unworked causeway. The pits are worked by the Amalgamated Roadstone Corporation. Figure 71 shows the section west of the road at 782883, opposite the entrance to Elliott's Pit. Thick flint gravel is overlain by an earthy bed showing podsol development, its upper layers grey and barren, with gingery-brown iron enriched horizons below. This is part of the extensive Moreton gravel terrace of Pleistocene (Ice) Age. A second section, in undamaged Tertiary materials, is the one next to the Dorchester-Wareham railway line north-west of Red Bridge 785887. Here current-bedded grey quartz sands reveal river channels and other features.

Since worked-out pits are easily graded and quickly reclaimed by the heathland, they can be difficult to spot. The Warmwell Sand & Gravel pits on North Heath commenced by the B3390 but have now moved west towards Knighton Heath Wood. In the present working areas depth is controlled by the level of the Empool valley bottom. Flooding results if the pits are taken below that level. Thick deposits of evenly graded sand are worked at present. The general dip of the beds is northerly. Close to Mayers Pond Plantation a 6–9m clay bed comes in and north again, into the old aerodrome of Woodsford Heath, a 3·5m cover of gravel. The latter is already being worked there, but there is no deeper development as yet. Sand working will extend north into the reserves under the airfield in the future.

Across the Empool valley at Broadmayne and West Knighton was another brickmaking area. Six pits were dug along Watergate Lane, in Reading Beds, where the latter surface close to the south side of the heathland syncline. Broadmayne pits produced rather drab brown bricks, speckled by manganese nodules in the clays. Now disused and reclaimed, the pits were the main local source of bricks and tiles. The industry was here from 1724 to 1939. Important as a source for Dorchester, the pits still used seventeenth-century methods and declined through being undersold by Chickerell products (page 51). Barclays Bank, No 6 High Street East and No 52 High Street West are among eighteenth-century Dorchester buildings displaying Broadmayne brickwork. The six yards produced 200,000 bricks per kiln per year, ie eight firings of 25,000. Each firing yielded 12,000 best speckled bricks, 6,000 hard red, 6,000 soft red and 1,000 wasters. The raw clay occurred in three 3m beds, red at the top, then ferruginous brown, with a white clay/sand mix at the base. An odd feature of tile making here was that bakers would not have speckled oven tiles—they said these burnt the bread!

Only the upper part of the Bagshot Beds outcrop around Warmwell, Moreton and Broadmayne, equivalents of the Pipe Clay Series and Agglestone Grit to the east. An interesting feature of the beds here in the western heaths is the fact that they also contain abundant chalk flints, Greensand chert pebbles with sponge spicules, and silicified Purbeck limestone fragments with *Cyrena*. This means that, when the beds were deposited, uplift somewhere nearby had allowed erosion right down through the chalk, Greensand and Wealden to the Purbeck limestone. This source may have been west of the present Dorset coast, or to the south, the Purbeck pebbles being added to the river system flowing in with its debris from SW England.

HARDY'S MONUMENT

The Bagshot Beds overstep the Reading Beds completely and rest directly on the chalk only a short distance west of Broadmayne at Little Mayne Farm. Beyond that point outliers occur at Bincombe Down, at 676857, where the deposit was worked for railway ballast, at 676865, and there are several others around Winterborne Came and west of Maiden Castle. However, the biggest outlier is the one on Black Down and at (Admiral) Hardy's Monument, 12·8km west of the main Bagshot outcrops.

Inspection of the old gravel pits around the monument reveals an unexpectedly coarser deposit than anything seen in the heathlands. These angular beds are presumed to be Bagshot Beds because they contain the same south-west, Greensand and Purbeck material as at Warmwell. About 2·6 sq km of chalk is covered at Black Down, but the beds appear more extensive than this because of downhill slumping. Good contrasts in vegetation, rough heath as opposed to pasture fields help in mapping the boundary, especially towards Bronkham Hill. Records show that some of the local uneven pitting of the surface is due to gravels collapsing over solution hollows in the chalk rather than to old diggings.

In places on the top of Black Down the base of the gravels has been strongly cemented, due to the chalk below, forming a tough conglomerate or puddingstone. Blocks of this occur well beyond the present outcrop, probably let down by erosion of the gravels when the cap was more extensive, or slumped down into neighbouring valleys during head formation in cold conditions. Resembling sitting sheep, they are known as grey wethers or sarsens, and west of Blackdown give rise to the name the Valley of Stones. Many examples have slumped far down from the present outcrops, eg Portesham village. Early man collected them for cromlechs, eg the Grey Mare and Her Colts, and circles such as Nine Stones, west of Winterbourne Abbas.

CHAPTER 15

Periclines and Faults

The boundary between the chalk downlands and the Weymouth lowland is one of the most deceptive areas geologically in the whole of Dorset. Hidden beneath its grassy slopes, farmlands and villages is the most structurally complex area of the county, an area described by the late W. J. Arkell as 'unique in the South of England for variety, intensity . . . and interest'. The features of the area are shown on Figure 72. Broadly the study of the area can be divided into two: west of Upwey where faulting is the main feature and east of Upwey where the faults are bounded by a string of periclines around Sutton Poyntz, Poxwell and Chaldon. Exposures are limited and, as with so much Dorset geology, the record has been built up by the accumulation of evidence over many years, from trenches dug for water etc, special boreholes drilled in search of oil, and much digging of special pits and augering across important areas.

The complexity of the area stems from the fact that it has features derived from both main periods of earth movements involved in Dorset—the intra-Cretaceous and the Tertiary activity referred to in Chapter 1. Each period of earth movement was characterised by its own particular style. The intra-Cretaceous upheavals could obviously only affect rocks already formed, ie the Jurassic material. These beds were fractured by faults with a southward downthrow, the most important one of all being the east-west Abbotsbury Fault, maximum displacement 450m. In the later Tertiary movements, however, faulting was characterised by northward downthrows—and this is where the complexity begins. Almost the same line occupied by the Abbotsbury Fault now developed a new fracture, the Ridgeway Fault. Superimposed on the older disturbance, the Ridgeway is a reversed fault thrusting

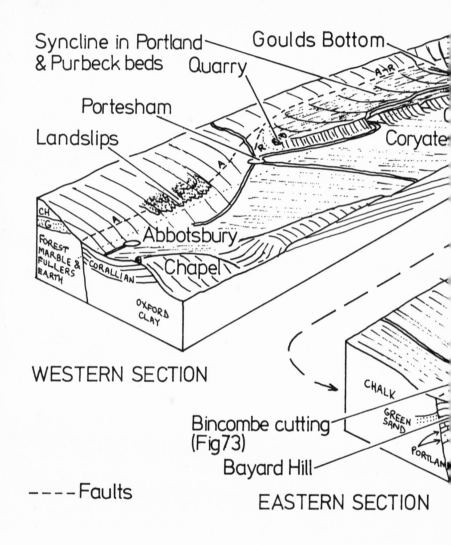

Syncline in Portland
& Purbeck beds

Goulds Bottom

Quarry

Portesham

Landslips

A-R

Coryate

CH
G

FOREST
MARBLE &
FULLERS
EARTH

CORALLIAN

Abbotsbury

Chapel

OXFORD
CLAY

WESTERN SECTION

CHALK

Bincombe cutting
(Fig73)

GREEN
SAND

Bayard Hill

PORTLAND

----Faults

EASTERN SECTION

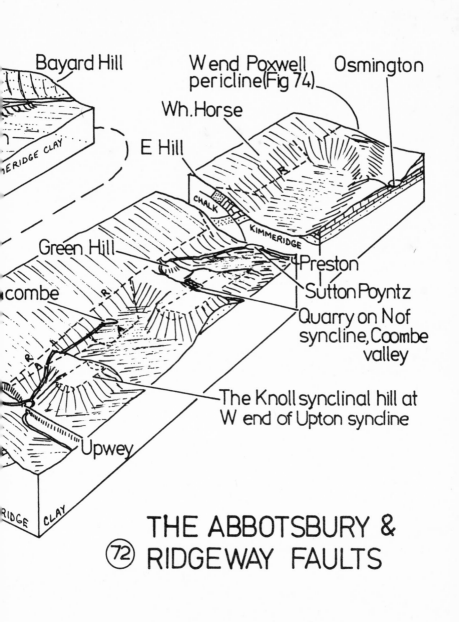

Bayard Hill

W end Poxwell pericline(Fig 74)

Osmington

Wh.Horse

E Hill

MERIDGE CLAY

CHALK

KIMMERIDGE

Green Hill

Preston

combe

Sutton Poyntz

Quarry on N of syncline, Coombe valley

The Knoll synclinal hill at W end of Upton syncline

Upwey

RIDGE CLAY

THE ABBOTSBURY &
72 RIDGEWAY FAULTS

the rocks back up again 61m towards the north. Both faults have been identified along most of the 24km of country between Abbotsbury and Chaldon.

Only the earlier southward downthrowing fault is recognised near Abbotsbury, bringing Corallian Beds against Fullers Earth and Forest Marble beds in the little valley north of the road to Abbotsbury Gardens and Chesil Beach. At the higher of the Abbotsbury iron ore exposures, Jubilee Copse (page 59), the fault crosses the slopes a little farther up the lane. The iron ore is brought against Forest Marble which can be identified in field rubble. The fault can also be located higher up the valley from the Red Lane ore exposure, near 573856. East of Abbotsbury the fault is hidden by Upper Greensand material collapsing down over the present-day slopes from its north side. 0·8km west of Portesham, the landslips end and the Ridgeway Fault now makes its appearance, cutting along the north side of the minor syncline between Portesham and Upwey. The syncline is called the Upwey syncline. Its south rim exposes the Portland and Purbeck Beds and there are several sites of interest.

First examine the old Portesham Quarry, by the farm track at 611859. The upper part of the Portland Stone and the Lower Purbeck Beds are exposed here. Large tufa-encrusted tree trunks from the Lower Purbeck have been left lying in the workings.

The lane east follows the base of the Portland-Purbeck rim of the syncline. West of Corton Hill it turns north into the syncline by means of a river gap cut through the rim at Coryates, and in the valley side here 18m of Portland Sand are partly exposed. The lane then keeps close to the north or dip slope of the rim, until it reaches another notable gap leading south to Corton Farm. This much narrower breach exposes the next beds up in the Portland Sand sequence, strong cementstones with *Exogyra* scattered through them and casts of many other fossils. A detailed succession is given on pages 125–6 of the Bridport and Yeovil Memoir. The main part of the vertical walled cutting is a 3·5m cementstone, known as the Scar Cementstone because locally it forms scars along the south scarp slope of the ridge. Continuing east, the lane leaves the south rim of the syncline and runs over the Lower and Middle Purbeck Beds in its centre. North of Upwey it joins the B3519 descending Goulds Bottom. Overgrown quarries in this valley used to reveal the Purbeck Beds close to the line where they are faulted against the Cretaceous by the Ridgeway Fault. The two fault lines coincide in this area and their disturbance can be located a short distance east at Bincombe railway cutting.

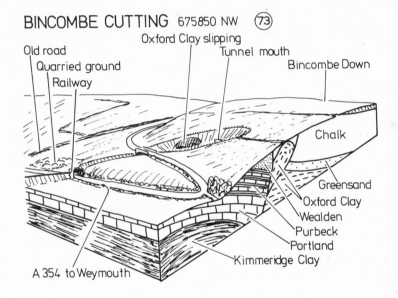

BINCOMBE CUTTING 675850 NW (73)

Oxford Clay slipping

Old road
Quarried ground
Railway
Tunnel mouth
Bincombe Down
Chalk
Greensand
Oxford Clay
Wealden
Purbeck
Portland
Kimmeridge Clay
A 354 to Weymouth

BINCOMBE CUTTING

At this famous locality the A354 and the railway are intertwined as the former twists and turns up Ridgeway Hill, first passing beneath and then over the rail route. Make for the upper bridge where a view north into the railway cutting can be obtained. The fault zone crosses this section as a double feature just north of the halfway point between the bridge and the tunnel mouth. Notice how the bank is slumping away, particularly on the west side. Figure 73 shows how this is due to a wedge of Oxford Clay. When the beds on the south side of the Abbotsbury Fault were pushed back upwards and northwards by the Ridgeway Fault, they broke away a sliver of Oxford Clay and Corallian material and brought it up with them. The northern part of this Oxford Clay outcrop is in the Red Nodule Beds with *Gryphaea dilatata*. The Corallian present is Nothe Grit. The result has been a continual source of trouble to the railway ever since the cutting was made, eg in 1934–5 a large amount came down on the line.

BINCOMBE AND SUTTON POYNTZ

The fault features become still more complicated east of this area since there is evidence that the Tertiary fold movements bent the older Abbotsbury fracture back north until, near Sutton Poyntz, its plane has become nearly horizontal! A glance at map 342 shows that the eastern section of the long zone of disturbance is closely associated with a chain of elongated domes or periclines. At each of these structures the beds dip outwards in all directions, with the oldest beds involved revealed in the centre of the feature. Around Bincombe and Sutton Poyntz the pattern of outcrops is complicated by a third factor—fault-bounded inliers of Oxford Clay, Cornbrash and Forest Marble Beds, caught between the now diverging paths of the two main fractures. The Abbotsbury Fault bounds them on the south, while the Ridgeway Fault passes through the chalk downs on the north. The combined result of all these factors is evident in the physical position of Bincombe village, which lies in a hollow of pastureland on Oxford Clays, bounded by Cretaceous slopes to the north and by enclosing arms of Portland and Purbeck Beds in the Knoll and Chalbury Down.

Refer again to Figure 72. The Knoll and Chalbury Down are seen to be synclinal continuations of the Upton Syncline which bounds the south side of both the Sutton Poyntz and Poxwell periclines. A good transect can be made from Chalbury Lodge (697828) up Coombe Valley to Green Hill. The route commences in Kimmeridge Clay and rises steeply up the edge of the rocks as they dip north into the Upton syncline. By the time the large quarry east of the road is reached, you have crossed the axis of the syncline for the Portland and Lower Purbeck beds revealed there are dipping south. The complete succession is exposed, the upper Portland Beds being more chalky than on the Isle of Portland.

On the right beyond the quarry the valley opens out, giving views east over the Sutton Poyntz pericline. The axis of the pericline runs through this area and the beds seen dipping south at the quarry now turn over to dip north into Green Hill on the far side of the little flat.

Take the footpath up over the valley side to the west. A track can be followed back to Bincombe village. It provides a good view of the synclinal Knoll farther west. Along this track 246m before Bincombe Church a quarry exposes Upper Greensand and the Cenomanian basement bed of the Chalk—the latter only fossiliferous now if you are prepared to dig. Remember that the two main faults pass to north and south and are not concerned just here. The beds in this quarry are unconformable on the Oxford Clays surrounding the village.

Return to the top of the Coombe Valley, to the lane junction immediately beyond Greenhill Barton. The Ridgeway Fault passes across the col here, approximately on the line of the road down to Sutton Poyntz. A pit in the field 36m south-east of the junction reveals recrystallised chalk, affected by its proximity to the fault. The road down to Sutton Poyntz passes over Portland Beds outcropping on the far side of the fault. The Portland Sand, exposed in the high left bank, contains *Exogyra nana*. Further details of the area are given in the Weymouth Memoir (see Bibliography).

Bent nearly horizontal by Tertiary fold movements, the Abbotsbury Fault produces two further tectonic inliers north and northeast of Sutton Poyntz. Both can be traced by stream sections and augering. For example, take the path north from the waterworks 705839. The first field is in Kimmeridge Clay with a low mound near the far gateway marking an old prospect for the Kimmeridge oil shale. In the second field, however, Cornbrash fossils in the field rubble confirm that the Abbotsbury Fault has been crossed on to its upthrown side.

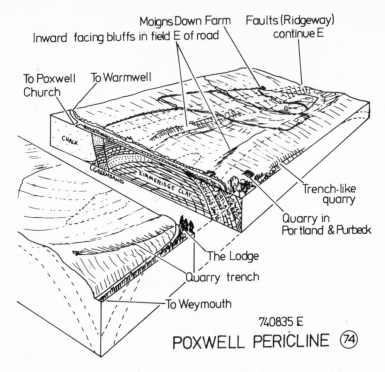

Moigns Down Farm   Faults (Ridgeway)
Inward facing bluffs in field E of road   continue E

To Poxwell   To Warmwell
Church

CHALK

GREENSAND   KIMMERIDGE CLAY

Trench-like
quarry

Quarry in
Portland & Purbeck

The Lodge
Quarry trench
To Weymouth

740835 E
POXWELL PERICLINE ⑭

POXWELL PERICLINE

   This structure is possibly the finest small example of an eroded
pericline anywhere in Britain. Elongated east-west it has a double
centre, each one revealing Kimmeridge Clay while Portland and
Purbeck Beds form the denuded rims. The presence of useful
building stones in the structure led to long ditch-like quarries
being worked along the outcrops. These have added to the
periclinal appearance, especially from the air. Travelling east
along the A353, the road reaches the structure just east of the
Upton Lane junction. Parking is impossible here so approach the
area on foot and take the footpath which begins near The Lodge
and runs on east to Moigns Down. Just inside the gate a small
quarry exposes the top of the Portland Stone and the basal 3·5m
of the Purbeck. *Hydrobia* moulds can be collected from the lowest
Purbeck bed and there are lenticular masses of tufa with silicified

tree trunks in the next 1m above it. Long grassy ditches run on east where outcrop was worked along the strike. The path can be continued through to Holworth Lane. By car, continue east along the A353.

Immediately after passing The Lodge, the road turns north through the rim and crosses the western centre of the pericline. Both the structure and the Ridgeway Fault bounding its north side are crossed before reaching the village.

CHALDON PERICLINE

This pericline is less deeply eroded at present. Only a small area of Jurassic beds (Middle and Upper Purbeck) has been revealed around 784838. The main floor of the oval hollow is Wealden material, with Gault Clay, Upper Greensand and Chalk forming the enclosing slopes. A small chalk quarry on the north-west of Lords Barrow, seen when driving up from the main road, exposes the *coranguinum* zone yielding characteristic sea-urchins. There is a good view of the pericline from the west at 768851, Holworth Lane.

Chaldon Herring marks the east end of the long belt of faulting and folding extending from the west coast near Abbotsbury. If the disturbances continue east, they are hidden beneath the chalk downlands but, as described in Chapter 10, the major anticlinal feature of the Weymouth area together with its complex margin is believed to continue en echelon to the south in the Purbeck fold.

CHAPTER 16

Recent Coastal Features: Chesil and Poole

The Dorset coast contains two remarkable recent geological features: Chesil Beach and Poole Harbour. Chesil Beach (Saxon: *Cisel*=shingle) is unique in Europe and one of three major shingle structures around the coasts of Britain.

FACTS AND THEORIES ABOUT CHESIL BEACH

Chesil Beach is 16km long from Portland to the head of The Fleet at Abbotsbury, but some regard the beach as starting at Bridport Harbour. Burton Mere, 510878, is a feature of the west end which suggests that the beach was originally offshore there, as it still is at The Fleet, and has since moved inland to abut the coast. The beach varies in width between 150 and 200m where it encloses The Fleet, but is slightly narrower to east and west. The crest is remarkably regular everywhere, with a gradual increase towards Portland where it is 14·7m above sea-level. The irregularly shaped Fleet varies from 900m wide to less than 100m in the Wyke narrows.

The seaward slopes of Chesil often carry the stepped profiles of storm-cut beaches. These survive for varying periods until chance combinations of wind and tidal height occur to reshape them. It seems that the beach is now fairly static in terms of the material in it—estimated at 50–100 million tonnes—and that shingle dredged from it in storms returns shortly afterwards under the effects of long-period ground swell. Accounts of past breaches under storm conditions are believed to be unreliable, but there are records of seawater a metre or so deep in meadows at Abbotsbury when waves overtopped the bank, and cases of ships being lifted on to the ridge. If figures of early surveys are reliable they suggest the beach has increased in width and height over the centuries.

The inner slopes of Chesil show evidence that (a) the beach is advancing slowly inland, rolling over itself as pebbles are thrown over its crest by storms (b) that seawater penetrates through the ridge at high tide forming hollows or seepage cans, very well developed opposite the army boat-training centre at Wyke Regis, 647774. The saltwater seepage adds to the brackish character of The Fleet, particularly at the Abbotsbury end which is nearly tideless. The tidal entrance is Small Mouth at the east end.

New borehole information shows that there is a fairly constant bedrock slope from the inner shore of The Fleet seawards beneath the beach. The seaward gradient of the beach is fairly constant, continuing at the general angle seen above the low-water mark until about 70m offshore but then more gently downwards until at 270m the depth is 11–18m below sea-level. Wide variations in the contents of boreholes have prevented correlations being made. The deposits found include shingle, clays, peaty clays and peat layers, the carbon content of the latter being the best help in dating events, below.

Views about the beach have included evolution on a bar of clay as a bay bar. Some writers thought that this clay feature was the same general shape as the beach above it, others that it inhibited the landward movement of the beach. Others believed the clay bar was destroyed and the beach is only a bay bar, pushed back against the coast behind it.

Changes in the height and recession of the beach, referred to already, have undoubtedly occurred; both are slow processes. The more spectacular claims made in the past were based on much greater short-term variations, but it is the long-term trend which is important. Hence the reason why other early observers were puzzled by the apparent lack of action in some respects, eg Smeaton wondered why recession was not obvious if quantities of material were being thrown over the crest. The amount of vegetation on the backslope has also featured in discussions. A lack of it was claimed as evidence of more rapid retreat at the Portland end, that the beach there was still not adjusted to a stable shoreline curve. But larger pebble sizes and hence greater porosity at that end may simply mean that plant life has been less successful in gaining a footing.

A third area of discussion has centred on the origin of the pebbles in Chesil. A wide range of ideas has been put forward. The beach mainly contains flints and quartzites, with South-West England material in the form of quartzites, granite and porphyry pebbles. Differences of view surround how this material travelled to the beach, whether former land areas out in West Bay were responsible and, particularly, the relationship of Chesil to the raised beach on the Isle of Portland (Chapter 6). The latter has been a crucial point since the raised beach platform at 7·6–18·3m above sea-level falls within the maximum height of Chesil, 14·7m, and the two are similar in composition. This suggests Chesil existed at the time the raised beach was formed and traces its origins back beyond present sea-level. If the raised beach was slightly older than Chesil and originally more extensive westward towards Devon, did its destruction form the source of the Chesil material? Flint and Greensand chert are present in both and the far-travelled 'South-West' rocks, but on Chesil the latter are of larger size. There is also plenty of Bunter quartzite from the Budleigh Salterton Pebble Beds of East Devon (*Geology Explained in South and East Devon*, pages 128–33). How did the mixture come about?

IDEA: The material is derived from the destruction of Tertiary gravel deposits, westerly extensions of the present heathlands covering lost land in West Bay.

ANSWER: None of the Tertiary gravels contain Budleigh Salterton Pebble Bed material.

IDEA: The 'SW' material crossed the floor of West Bay.

ANSWER: Geophysical work has shown that the bay floor is mainly solid rock outcrop with very little loose sediment on it.

IDEA: Longshore drift cannot account for the 'SW' materials or the Budleigh Salterton Pebble Bed quartzites since shingle could not pass obstructions such as Otterton Point and Beer Head in East Devon.

ANSWER: Since the beach originated prior to present sea-level it could be derived from longshore drift on former coasts south of the present one. That coast would also have had its obstructive headlands, but as each was eroded away a further stream of shingle would be allowed to continue its eastward journey. In this way the Budleigh Salterton Pebble Beds and the Tertiary gravels could have been eroded from separate outcrops in those former land areas and mixed together en route.

THE FLEET

The histories of The Fleet and Chesil are intimately linked. In recent years The Fleet has yielded new evidence, information which can be related to some of the ideas noted above and allow a tentative order of events to be constructed.

The Fleet is 13km long, an estuarine lagoon filled with extensive mudflats. At low water its remaining channels average 0·3–1m depth with deeper areas at Wyke narrows, 2·5m, and at Small Mouth, 5·5m, both maintained by tidal scouring. The whole lagoon is brackish, a state partly maintained by seepage through Chesil. An attempt to reclaim The Fleet was made in 1630. A dam with sluices was built, probably near Small Mouth, but the project failed because of the seepage.

The landward shore of the Fleet has clearly never been attacked by the sea. Its varying outline is the result of the limestone and clay geology of the Weymouth anticline, the limestones forming promontories trimmed into low cliffs by subaerial erosion and small waves within The Fleet. The clays form the featureless bays and inlets, and everywhere along the shore there is a scarcity of Chesil type pebbles. Their appearance around the Langton Herring ferry point is due to human activity—bringing them over to create a firmer landing area.

The streams flowing into The Fleet are small and supply very little sediment. The lagoon is a sediment trap but the great amount it contains has come from earlier times. The small streams do not provide sufficient flow to flush this out and the slow landward advance of Chesil will not bury it for a long time yet. On the floor of The Fleet 2·5m of unoxidised blue-grey mud is generally present, with a red-brown oxidised layer below. The lower layer has been attributed to a subaerially weathered land surface just prior to the submergence of The Fleet by the sea.

The most interesting recent information obtained from The Fleet concerns its submerged peat deposits, their pollen content, and radiocarbon dating obtained from them. In boreholes, peat beds have been found at 2–5m below sea-level. The deposits, generally less than 3m thick, contain mainly *Phragmites* (water reed) peat with a little pine pollen. Under Chesil there is a much higher pine-pollen grain content, and fragments of *Phragmites* peat cast up on the seaward slopes of the beach near Abbotsbury (1970) also revealed a high *Alnus* (alder) pollen content. Radiocarbon dates from all these materials give ages ranging between 4023 ± 50 to 5410±115 years ago, ie The Fleet and Chesil areas were reedy swamps with pine and alder growing nearby at that period.

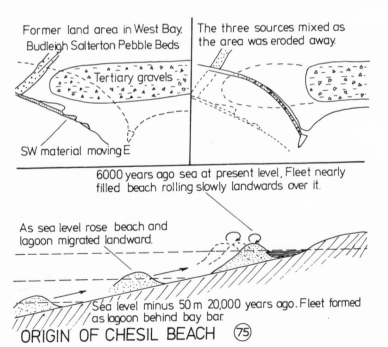

Former land area in West Bay. Budleigh Salterton Pebble Beds

The three sources mixed as the area was eroded away.

Tertiary gravels

SW material moving E

6000 years ago sea at present level, Fleet nearly filled beach rolling slowly landwards over it.

As sea level rose beach and lagoon migrated landward.

Sea level minus 50 m 20,000 years ago. Fleet formed as lagoon behind bay bar.

ORIGIN OF CHESIL BEACH   (75)

EVOLUTION OF CHESIL BEACH AND THE FLEET

Obviously the story of these two features is not fully known and much work remains to be done. At present it seems that the beach began as a bay bar along the coast of former lands in West Bay. As this old coast was modified and worn back destruction of its outcrops and headlands combined with longshore drift to mix Tertiary gravels (already containing 'SW' material, of course) and Budleigh Salterton Pebble Bed quartzites and move them east. New additions of 'SW' rocks may have been made as well by longshore drift or by a more extensive glacial advance in one of the four cold phases of the Ice Age. Chesil was present, then, on an ancient coastline when, in the last interglacial warm phase of the Ice Age, sea-level was higher and the Portland raised beach with its similar materials was formed. Towards the end of the Ice Age when sea-level rose again in the Flandrian transgression of 20,000–6,000 years ago, The Fleet area was rapidly filled with sediment and became a reedy lagoon, surrounded by pine and alder trees. It advanced landwards ahead of the Chesil Beach, the rise of sea-level aiding the landward movement of the beach and, about 9,000 years ago, also submerging The Fleet. The area was then rapidly filled with sediments which were in position by about 5,000 years ago. The Fleet was left as a sediment trap with Chesil Beach still offshore over the bulk of its length, its rate of landward migration slowed considerably although it is still rolling over on itself, burying The Fleet beneath it as it does so.

Chesil and The Fleet are now 'fossil' structures. Little new sediment has entered The Fleet in the last 4,000 years. Chesil Beach now receives little additional material from the west due to the present coastal obstructions of Otterton Point and Beer Head.

Post Glacial Pollen Zones and Dates		Climate	Chesil and The Fleet
VIII	2,500 years ago—present	Sub Atlantic (Warmer)	Chesil continues to protect mainland shore and migrate towards it.
VII B	5,000–2,500 years ago	Sub Boreal (Cooler)	Completion of infilling of Fleet.

Post Glacial Pollen Zones and Dates		*Climate*	*Chesil and The Fleet*
VII A	7,000–5,000 years ago	Atlantic (Warm)	Sea-level rise ends 6,000 years ago.
VI	9,000–7,000 years ago	Boreal (Cold)	Filling of Fleet with sand, silt and pebbles behind seaward shelter of 'Chesil' bay bar.
V	9,600–9,000 years ago	Boreal (Cold)	
IV	10,300–9,600 years ago	Pre-Boreal	Flandrian submergence in progress but Fleet shore protected by offshore 'Chesil' bar.

PEBBLE GRADING

Interesting changes in pebble size occur along Chesil Beach from pea size at Bridport to large cobbles near Chesilton—but the opposite grading should result from longshore drift east. The finer would be expected to travel farthest and this is in fact so below low water. The predominant tidal direction in any twenty-four hours is eastward along the beach and underwater the pebbles do become finer towards Portland, so why is the situation reversed on the beach slopes above? Experiments show that pebbles move to the area where they conform to the average size, ie are neither smaller and easily dredged out nor larger and more easily thrown up by the waves.

Large storm waves hit Chesil head-on or from the west and south-west, and in the latter cases drive the shingle eastwards. The beach is in fact at its highest directly in line with the straight gap west out into the Atlantic, ie where the largest uninterrupted waves meet it head-on. However, there are two sets of waves at work on Chesil and in calmer periods the wave direction is often from within the English Channel, from the south or south-east. These waves are only powerful enough to move smaller material—much of the larger stuff is thrown too high up the beach by westerly storms for them to reach it anyway. So the smaller material moves back north-west during quieter weather, thus reversing the grading above low water level.

Poole Harbour is basically a drowned river mouth, formed by the same recent post-glacial rise in sea-level involved in driving Chesil Beach ashore. Excavations at Hamworthy have revealed a fresh-water peat at minus 13m which dates from $7{,}340 \pm 110$ years ago. By coincidence Poole Harbour provides a modern sedimentary environment along the same alignment as the ancient river which carried the heathland sands and gravels eastwards in Tertiary times.

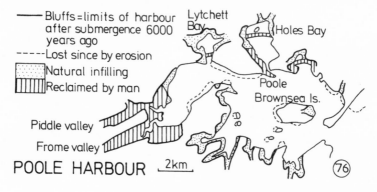

The greatest changes in the harbour in recent centuries have occurred on the north side by reclamation around Poole and by construction of railway embankments. These date from 1845–7 across Lytchett Bay, 1872 Creekmoor, 1874 Parkstone Bay, 1893 Holes Bay. Other major projects have been Poole power station and Turlin's Moor for housing. As a result the north-eastern areas of the harbour have now lost their natural coastline and remain the areas under the greatest pressure.

Natural factors reducing the harbour area are: (a) deposition of sediments from the Frome and other rivers which drain over 776 sq km of land, bringing in mainly Tertiary material during flood times, (b) growth of *Spartina townshendi* saltmarsh. It has been calculated that the reduction of the high water area of the harbour from 6,000 years ago, when the submergence was completed, down to 1807 was at the rate of 0·1 hectare per year. Since 1807 the rate has averaged 1·6 hectares per year. Very little erosion occurs in Poole Harbour at present. Its original outline can be traced by the low bluff 2–6m high on the landward side of the saltmarshes and reclaimed areas. Bluffs only exist at the waterside still in limited areas, eg Shipstal Point.

A major feature of interest at Poole are the spits which have built out since the harbour was formed. Whereas Chesil is the major shingle structure of the Dorset coast these are its main sand features. Rapid retreat of the Bournemouth-Christchurch coastline seems to be the chief source and the sand has accumulated by being driven onshore, forming dune ridges of white silica material with very little lime in it—an unusual feature in sea-derived sands.

Old maps show that three successive dune ridges have formed and been driven ashore since the sixteenth century. Little Sea is a former creek. Formed by the northward growth of a spit on the seaward side of the peninsula it then became an enclosed lagoon, still invaded by high tides at first, eventually so surrounded by dune ridges that it now forms an inland lake. Its western shore represents the original east coast of the peninsula, a coastline backed by land about 15m high, which can be traced south to Knoll House Hotel. North and east the original coastline probably continued in a broad curve to somewhere south of Hengistbury Head.

Like so many similar features, the story of the sandy peninsula has not been one of uninterrupted growth. Measured additions of 72m occurred on the seaward side, 1894–1924, but double that rate has been lost at the north end in Shell Bay. Building of the sea front drives at Bournemouth may have cut off the sand supply and caused a change to erosional activity at the north end.

CHAPTER 17

Marble and Stone

Much of Dorset's place in history and architecture is due to the stones with which the county is endowed. The Jurassic system has yielded varied and valuable building stones:

Jurassic system limestones:

Purbeck Beds	Freshwater and marine limestones of variable thickness; used in buildings, gardens; some when polished making fine 'marble' for decorative interior work.
Portland Beds	Fine marine limestones. Important in major public buildings where the white appearance and contrast is employed to set the building aside from its neighbours. Roach beds for strong, less visually demanding work, breakwaters, special cladding effects, etc.
Corallian	No important building stones.
Great Oolite	Source of the Bath Stone Series of the Cotswolds. Fullers Earth & Forest Marble
Inferior Oolite	Sherborne Building Stone, limeburning and general building, Ham Hill and Doulting Stone of Somerset, Painswick (Gloucestershire), Ancaster (Lincolnshire).
Lias Limestone	Cottage and garden walls only. Extensively used in the past for limeburning and cement making.

THE EARLY MARBLE INDUSTRY OF PURBECK

The Romans began to work Purbeck 'marble' soon after their conquest, and quickly achieved a considerable output of decorative work, inscriptive slabs, etc. After AD150 production continued on a more limited scale, to the fourth century. Roman items in Purbeck 'marble' have been discovered at Caerleon, Chester, Chichester, Cirencester, Colchester, Dorchester, London, Silchester and St Albans.

THE MARBLE TRADE IN THE MIDDLE AGES

A new upsurge in 'marble' working occurred between 1170 and 1350. Nearly every English church of any size built at this time had polished dressings of it, eg Westminster Abbey in 1256-7, Exeter Cathedral in 1309. Developing later into a trade in effigies the period was to last into the fifteenth century when alabaster figures came into vogue.

Purbeck 'marble' was employed in four principal ways in this period: in church buildings as decorative polished shafts set in Gothic clusters and in polished floor slabs and altar tables; in monumental effigies for royalty, bishops, abbots, lords and knights; in plainer coffin lids, and as the bases of monumental brasses.

In effigies, Purbeck marblers set the fashion, scouring their quarries for the large perfect blocks required. Mention has been made (Chapter 12) of the need to erect the beds on end to achieve long slender church columns. In the effigy trade the thin beds imposed a rather flat appearance, the longer-nosed or full-bosomed seldom got justice! However, an approximate dating is indicated by the fullness of the treatment—earlier figures are flatter and less realistic. Effigies seem to have been ordered without reference to the appearance of the individual commemorated. The earliest is that cut in the 1100s of Leofric, founder bishop of the diocese of Exeter, who died in 1072. Other early ones occur in Salisbury Cathedral, the porch of Abbotsbury Church, Tolpuddle and Sherborne Abbey. The overall output was perhaps only a few dozens. Many abbots' effigies were lost at the Dissolution and it seems geological sacrilege that some were painted! Perhaps the finest surviving figure is the thirteenth-century lady in Romsey Abbey.

Corfe Castle was the great manufacturing centre of the marble trade. Marblers' haulage tracks converged on the village from small quarries strung out along the south slopes of the vale— from Lynch, Scoles, Quarr, Wilkswood, Afflington, Dunshay, etc. The stone was brought in in a rough state along these trackways into the now dead-end West Street, which was the main street, lined with workshops and all the principal buildings of the community. The present main road, East Street, is a product of the turnpike era. Stocks of marble were kept in West Street— bankers as they were called—and all work left the village at least squared up or partly carved. Much of the work was completed there and the marblers were among the top craftsmen of the country. West Street now stands on a pile of chippings 1–2m thick. The ancient trade outlet was the right-of-way across Rempstone Heath to Ower Quay on Poole Harbour.

HISTORICAL ASPECTS OF THE BUILDING STONE TRADE

Although 'marble' was the high quality product, ordinary limestones were also in demand. Purbeck stone appears in early building records—for Winchester Castle in 1270—while in the sixteenth century it became a popular paving material in London, in 1650–60 over 10,300m of it was used.

Portland Stone had been used in Exeter Cathedral, the royal palace at Westminster, and the Tower of London in the fourteenth century, but it did not come into prominence until later. An inventory of stock-in-hand at London Bridge in 1350 recorded 518m of Portland Stone and 18 great stones of Beer (East Devon, see *Geology Explained in South and East Devon*, p. 142), but no fifteenth- or sixteenth-century accounts show any use of Portland Stone. The Portland trade began in earnest 1674–1700 when over 50,000 tonnes of the stone were used in rebuilding St Paul's Cathedral. It seems the delay was largely technical. The coarse cavernous roach beds on top of the stone were tough and, although they were regarded as good engineering material, they stood in the way of early development for architectural purposes. For Exeter Cathedral, St Paul's and other works the Whit or Base Bed stone was essential. Possibly the earliest trade was supplied from landslipped blocks, but at the time St Paul's was under construction technical troubles, such as the amount of overburden and the severe problem of getting the stone down to the shore, were very evident. For example, the St Paul's accounts show that over £2,000 was spent in 1696–8 on new ways and piers at Portland (page 74). The Portland industry differed from Purbeck's because the stone was usually sent away only squared up—only on rare occasions was carving done on the island and then carvers had to be brought in temporarily from London.

One feature of medieval life was to have a long and serious effect on Portland quarrying—the open field system. The situation was aggravated by the custom of dividing ownership of holdings equally among all heirs whenever a person died intestate. This resulted in people owning '⅛ of ¼ of ¼ of a quarry' or '¼ of ⅓ of 3yd of quarry land at . . .' and so on. The payment of royalty on quarry ground permission was a complicated affair! Portland still has its Court Leet and for a full account of its peculiar history see J. H. Bettey's *The Island and Royal Manor of Portland*.

In the early nineteenth century 20–30,000 tonnes were exported annually, 0·45cu m of stone making 1 tonne weight. In 1839 the annual production was estimated to equal 0·4 hectares of good stone and 808 hectares were believed to be unworked. The labour force at this period was 800 men with 180 horses and 50 ships. In the latter half of the nineteenth century a decline in the trade is illustrated by the tonnage carried on the Merchants' Railway, the principal but not the sole outlet—in 1865 over 81,000 tonnes carried, but in 1882 only 46,000 tonnes.

The Merchants' Railway can still be traced from Priory Corner, the hairpin bend on the main road above Fortuneswell, down to Castleton. It was opened in 1826. Despite the outlay during the rebuilding of St Paul's Cathedral, the island had right up to the early nineteenth century gone on using sleds to

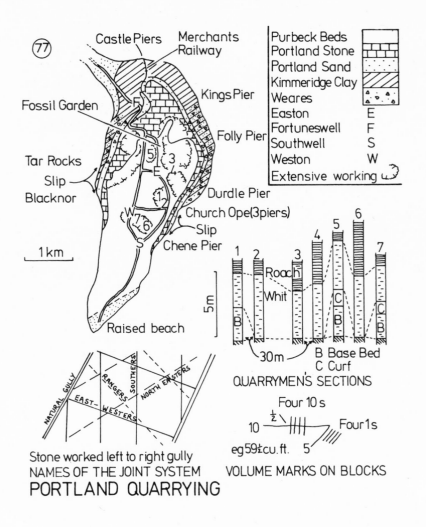

(77)

Castle Piers
Merchants Railway
Kings Pier
Folly Pier
Fossil Garden
Tar Rocks
Slip
Blacknor
Durdle Pier
Church Ope(3piers)
Slip
Chene Pier

1 km

Raised beach

Purbeck Beds	
Portland Stone	
Portland Sand	
Kimmeridge Clay	
Weares	
Easton	E
Fortuneswell	F
Southwell	S
Weston	W
Extensive working	ꙮ

Roach
Whit
B
1 2 3 4 5 6 7

5 m

30m
B Base Bed
C Curf
QUARRYMEN'S SECTIONS

NATURAL GULLY
RANGERS
SOUTHERS
NORTH EASTERS
EAST-WESTERS

Stone worked left to right gully
NAMES OF THE JOINT SYSTEM

Four 10 s
½
10 —\|||| Four 1s
eg 59½ cu. ft. 5
VOLUME MARKS ON BLOCKS

PORTLAND QUARRYING

Railway bridge over

THE MERCHANTS' RAILWAY INCLINE 686744 SE

let stone down to the piers—the usual system being to employ the friction of another block dragging over the ground behind, or a rear team of horses which were often pulled down the slope on their haunches. The Merchants' Railway incline continued in use until 1939, surviving as a cheap means of exporting stone, despite the arrival of a main railway line on the island in 1865 and its extension in 1902 to Church Ope and Easton, which necessitated the bridge over the bottom of the Merchants' Railway incline (Figure 78). The vast network of tramroads connecting to the head of the Merchants' Railway can still be traced through the quarry grounds. Many archways and bridges bear dated key-stones, illustrating the development dates of various sections.

THE PURBECK QUARRYING REVIVAL

With the demise of the 'marble' trade in the sixteenth century, Purbeck seems to have been in a relatively depressed state. In the early eighteenth century, however, the Purbeck trade appeared in new areas, so revitalised that through to the end of the nineteenth century any assessment as to which district was more important—Purbeck or Portland—would be well nigh impossible.

Swanage became the new centre; at that time it was a village clustered around a small creek which ran west close to the High Street. The first quarries were opened about 1700 along the slopes immediately to the south, running from Peveril Point to Cowlease and Townsend. During the eighteenth century the trade extended to the coastal outcrops in Durlston Bay and to the large-scale cliff workings in Portland Stone. About 1800, development of stone mines commenced in the original quarry belt, as the stone was followed deeper with the north dip of the Purbeck fold. In consequence, some parts of Swanage are close to mined ground and subsidence has sometimes occurred, eg in 1895 at the west end of Alexandra Terrace.

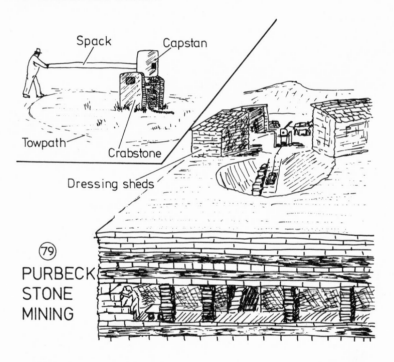

The Purbeck stone mines kept to a traditional pattern; a circular whim or horse-powered drum was set up for haulage, surrounded by three or four shelters where the stone was dressed (Figure 79). The whim's stone uprights survive as indicators of many old mine entrances. Underground in such variable beds it was essential to have a strong roof. Pillars of waste stone were built to support it as the workings were extended.

In the areas nearest Swanage the intensity of quarrying and mining soon exhausted almost every usable bed of stone. Leaving the hillside pockmarked, but green now that the grass has recovered it, the workings have ensured that Swanage could never extend far up the slopes and must develop north and west. The quarry lands are riddled with footpaths (see the 1:25000 map), but the old mine entrances and capstans may be hard to locate. Caravan sites cover some of the ground. For those who search the thickets diligently, the road up through the Priests Way site to California Farm passes several mine remains.

Impending exhaustion of the stone nearest the town caused the spread of the industry westwards along the outcrop to Langton Matravers and Acton at the beginning of the nineteenth century. At first nearness of the beds to the surface there offset the haulage costs to the Swanage quayside, but eventually mines were needed in these western areas as well, although they were never as deep as those nearest the town and were often worked by donkeys. The length of the spack (Figure 79) was said to indicate the depth of a mine. A 2m capstan with a 5m spack was reckoned to raise 1 tonne of stone 2m for every circuit the animal made.

The most bizarre aspect of the life of the community was use of the stone as currency in bartering! Quarrymen were paid in stone 'pennies', being 5.44kg (12lb) in weight, and there was also a 65kg (144lb) 'shilling'. They staggered home with these and traded them across shop counters which also had to be of stone to stand it! The system survived into the nineteenth century and shopkeepers' counters were known, like the quayside stockpiles, as bankers.

Through the narrow streets of this tough town with its cramped little cottages, the stone carts trundled in clouds of dust in summer or sticky mud in winter. They headed for the bankers, bringing about sixty 3 tonne loads a day. The bankers, long since disappeared, stretched along the south-east shore from the Mowlem to the little stone quay, the stone often piled over 3m high in them.

The export system was fantastically inefficient, each piece being handled up to five times before it was on board ship. From the bankers the stone was loaded on high-wheeled carts which were driven out into the sea. It was then loaded on to barges, each taking 6–9 tonnes and rowed by two men, who ferried the stone out to the coasting vessels lying farther offshore. All supplies inwards to Swanage—coal etc—came the same way since land connections were still poor for heavy goods. At least seventy stone barges were at work in the mid-nineteenth century. The only improvements made to the harbour in the stone-trade days were the old pier (1859) and a tramway from it along the bankers. The present pier extends more to the north than the old one did and dates from 1896.

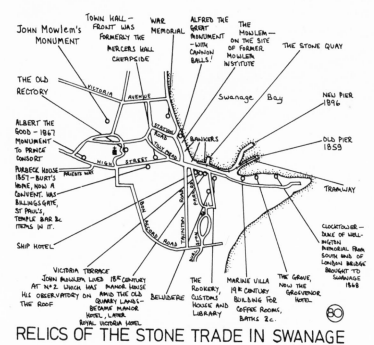

RELICS OF THE STONE TRADE IN SWANAGE

The trade declined 1885–96 and by the turn of the century The Parade and Institute Road had been built over. Yet the modern seaside town is still rich in the remains of its pre-tourist days. George Burt and his uncle, John Mowlem, (Chapter 7) foresaw the new role of Swanage and indulged in glorifying the place with bits and pieces of almost anything that would form a return cargo for the London stone boats. Among the more obvious are the Great Globe and the eccentricities of Durlston Castle, together with numerous metal street bollards with London foundry or parish names on them. The town also contains bits of the former London Bridge, Billingsgate Market, the Royal Exchange, Waterloo Bridge, Millbank Prison, the Mansion House, Pentonville, items from Trafalgar Square, Ludgate Circus, Cheapside and Greenwich! George Burt, the 'King of Swanage', almost operated a lend-lease system, quickly taking back anything that was no longer wanted (Figure 80). A fascinating account of this aspect of local history is given in *Curiosities of Swanage or Old London By The Sea* (Bibliography).

PORTLAND QUARRY WORKING

Today Portland is undoubtedly the major area of quarrying activity in Dorset. The usefulness of the beds on the isle is:

Top Rubble	Shingle		Light grey limestone. Up to 1·5m thick.
	Slat		Hard grey shaley limestone. Several beds, each about 60cm thick. Much used for dry walling on Portland itself.
	Bacon		Soft earthy limestones, totalling 1–2·5m.
	Tier &		Bacon is the local Portland name for fibrous
	Aish		calcite or beef. Aish was used for scrubbing ships decks.
	Soft Burr		Tufaceous limestone often containing the 'birds nests' or cycad stools. Burr means a rough lumpy rock.
	Dirt Bed		Black dirt. The fossil soil; no value, of course.
	Top Cap		Freshwater limestones 1·5–4·5m thick. Ground up for aggregate nowadays.
	Skull Cap		Grey-bown tufaceous limestone 0·45–1·5m

Lower Purbeck Beds

Portland Stone : Freestone Series	Roach	Tough grey-brown oolitic limestone full of fossil casts. Engineering use, special cladding effects. Roach is a widely used quarry name implying coarseness, unsuitability.
	Whit Bed	Literally, the White Bed. Buff-coloured oolitic limestone, large quantities of comminuted shells. A freestone. One of the principal stone beds.
	Flinty Bed	A chert bed up to 60cm. With the Curf it marks a brief return to the depositional conditions of the Cherty Series.
	Curf	Soft chalky limestone. Splits in all directions (stringers) when struck.
	Base Bed Roach	Shelly, oolitic. Up to 1m. Often absent.
	Base Bed	(Sometimes called Best Bed but the Whit Bed has generally been the best bed so this has caused much confusion). Soft white oolitic limestone, uniform texture, shells rare. A freestone. One of the two principal beds but not good for exterior work.
Portland Stone:	Cherty Series	No economic value formerly but now ground, cherts included, for aggregate.

Portland Stone varies greatly from place to place because of its shallow-water origin. Quarries within 30m of each other may exhibit quite differing thicknesses in various units, while a second vital aspect of the stone is its joint pattern (Figure 77). The joints played an important role in the development of quarry faces which would be worked from the left gully to the right one in the diagram for ease of wedging out. In recent years the names Top, Middle and Bottom Tier have gained some favour over the terms Whit Bed and Base Bed. The overburden is also known as Top Rubble, Bottom Rubble and Caps, the first two being dug by excavators and the latter usually blasted for use in aggregate like the Cherty Series.

Scappling over the surface, as described by Smeaton, is avoided in modern work as it makes the selection of good stones more difficult. Much finished shaping is now accomplished by machines, and hand carving is reserved only for tasks machines cannot manage. Chiselled finishes, allowing handwork marks to remain and deliberately making them over machined areas, give a 'period' appearance to stone but allow it to collect soot and rainwater and become damaged. The best weather-resisting finish is the gritted one, a smooth surface with all hand and machine marks sanded off. The compact and semi-crystalline structure of Portland Stone helps it to resist blistering fairly well, but on flat ledges in buildings it becomes vulnerable, as all limestones will, to rainwater and sulphuric acid forming calcium sulphate crusts. These involve a change in volume and the skin blisters off as a result.

It is still possible to see carving being done for church repairs, gravestones and special requirements at Easton Masonry works, but the bulk of the modern trade is very different in character. Portland Stone is now mainly used as sawn slabs, cladding the exteriors of buildings—a reflection of the change in building design to steel frame structures. Even worse, from the old craftsman's viewpoint, is the manufacture of simulated Portland Stone in concrete mouldings and panels. These ground-up Portland materials do keep the colour of the stone and, it must be admitted, would cost the earth today if they had to be carved out. They are cast ready to groove and lock into each other, and are simply bolted on to the framework of the structure. The main centre for these products is at Weston.

The different names given to the Portland Beds in Purbeck have been indicated in Figure 19. For a fascinating account of the quarry names of both districts see Arkell 1945 (Bibliography).

PURBECK QUARRYING

In this century the Purbeck trade has become a solely opencast industry, much of its task achieved by mechanical excavators. The industry is much smaller than it was in terms of numbers of quarries and men involved, yet it is healthy and busy, producing house and garden walling, rockery and crazy-paving stone. Whereas mining removed only the valuable veins, opencast working affects the appearance of the area more severely until the excavations are back-filled with waste and become grassed over.

In addition to quarries described in Chapter 12, the Acton and Langton districts provide many other active or recent sites.

It is one of the ironies of man's relationship to the geological heritage that he creates the worst landscape scars where he seeks materials for his greatest cultural and aesthetic achievements. Portland has suffered most, largely because its stone is massive. Luckily the Purbeck Beds, being thinner, have always been more easily dug and back-filled, leaving less conspicuous scars. Portland excepted, Dorset remains remarkably unspoilt and has an abundance of superb landscapes. The county's rocks, whose story must be measured in millions of years, have formed the foundation of a human history spanning only a few thousands. Understanding our own place in the time-scale of the earth gives the appreciation and care of our geological heritage a deeper meaning. Dorset, as a whole, richly deserves both our appreciation and our care.

Bibliography and References

PDNH&AS —Proceedings Dorset Natural History & Archaeological Society

GENERAL INTEREST: GEOLOGY

Ager, D. V. *Introducing Geology* (Faber, 1975)
Arkell, W. J. *The Jurassic System in Great Britain* (Oxford, 1933)
Black, Rhona M. *Elements of Palaeontology* (Cambridge, 1970)
 Caenozoic Fossils (British Museum, Natural History, 1975)
Calder, Nigel *Restless Earth* (BBC, 1972)
Hamilton, Woolley & Bishop. *Minerals Rocks & Fossils* (Hamlyn, 1974)
Kurten, Bjorn. *The Age of Dinosaurs* (World Univ Library, 1968)
 Mesozoic Fossils (British Museum, Natural History, 1975)
Swinton, W. E. *Fossil Amphibians & Reptiles* (British Museum, Natural History, 1965)
——. *Dinosaurs* (British Museum, Natural History, 1969)
Tarling, D. H. & M. P. *Continental Drift* (Bell; Penguin, 1972)
Whitten, D. G. A. & Brooks, J. R. V. *Dictionary of Geology* (Penguin, 1972)

GENERAL INTEREST: DORSET

Bettey, J. H. *The Island & Royal Manor of Portland* (Court Leet & Univ of Bristol, 1970)
Cochrane, C. *Poole Bay & Purbeck*, 2 vols (Friary Press, Dorchester, 1970, 1971)
Legg, R. *Purbeck Island* (Dorset Publishing Co, Milborne Port, 1972)

Taylor, C. *Dorset* (Hodder & Stoughton, 1970)

Wightman, R. *Portrait of Dorset* (Hale, 1968)

Victoria County History

DORSET GEOLOGY: SHORT LIST OF REFERENCES AND PAPERS

Ager, D. V. & Smith, W. E. *Coast of S Devon & Dorset Between Branscombe and Burton Bradstock*, Geologists' Assoc Guide No 23 (1973)

Arber, M. A. 'The Coastal Landslips of W Dorset,' *Proc Geol Assoc*, 52 (1941) 273–83

Arkell, W. J. 'The Portland Beds of the Dorset Mainland,' *Proc Geol Assoc*, 46 (1935) 301–47

——. 'The Tectonics of the Purbeck & Ridgeway Faults, Dorset,' *Geol Mag*, 73 (1936) 56–73 and 97–118

——. 'Dorset Geology 1930–40,' *PDNH&AS*, 61 (1940) 117–35

——. 'The Names of the Strata in the Purbeck & Portland Stone Quarries of Dorset,' *PDNH&AS* (1945) 158–68

——. 'The Structure of Spring Bottom Ridge and the Origin of the Mud-slides at Osmington Dorset,' *Proc Geol Assoc*, 62 (1951) 21–30

Arkell, W. J. et al, *Geology of the Country Around Weymouth, Swanage, Corfe and Lulworth*, Mem Geol Surv (HMSO, 1947)

Benfield, E. *Purbeck Shop* (Cambridge, 1940)

Bird, E. C. F. 'The Physiography of The Fleet,' *PDNH&AS*, 93 (1971) 119–24

Brown, P. E. 'Algal Limestones & Associated Sediments in the Basal Purbeck of Dorset,' *Geol Mag* 100 (1963) 565–73

Calkin, J. B. *Ancient Purbeck* (Friary Press, Dorchester, 1968)

Calkin, J. B. & Lewer, D. *Curiosities of Swanage or Old London by the Sea* (Friary Press, Dorchester, 1971)

Carr, A. P. & Blackley, M. W. L. 'Geological Composition of the Pebbles of Chesil Beach,' *PDNH&AS*, 90 (1960) 133–40

——. 'Ideas on the Origin & Development of Chesil Beach,' *PDNH&AS*, 95 (1973) 9–17

——. 'Investigations bearing on the Age and Development of Chesil Beach,' *Trans Inst British Geogrs*, 58 (1973) 99–109

Casey, R. 'The Stratigraphical Palaeontology of the Lower Greensand,' *Palaeontology* 3 (1961) 487–621

——. 'Dawn of the Cretaceous,' *Bull SE Union Sci Socs*, 117 (1963) 1–15

Chatwin, C. P. *The Hampshire Basin*, British Regional Geology (HMSO, 1960)

Conway, B. W. *The Black Ven Landslip, Charmouth, Dorset*, Inst Geol Sciences Report 74/3 (HMSO, 1974)

Curry, D. *The Geology of the Southampton Area*, Geologists' Assoc. Guide No 14 (1958)

Davies, G. M. *The Dorset Coast, A Geological Guide* (A & C Black, 1956; unrevised reprint of 1935 edition)

Delair, J. B. 'The Mesozoic Reptiles of Dorset,' *PDNH&AS*, 79 (1958) 47–72 and 80 (1959), 52–89

Denness, B. *The Reservoir Principle of Mass Movement*, Inst Geol Sciences Report 72/7 (HMSO, 1972)

Donovan, D. T. & Stride, A. H. 'An Acoustic Survey of the Sea Floor S of Dorset and its Geological Interpretation,' *Phil Trans Roy Soc Series B.* 244 (1961) 299–330

Hallam, A. 'A Sedimentary & Faunal Study of the Blue Lias of Dorset & Glamorgan,' *Phil Trans Roy Soc Series B* 243 (1960) 1–41

Hallam, A. 'Origin of the Limestone Shale Rhythm in the Blue Lias of England,' *Jour Geol*, 72 (1964) 157–69

Highley, D. E. *Ball Clay*, Mineral Resources Dossier No 11 (HMSO, 1975)

House, M. R. 'The Structure of the Weymouth Anticline,' *Proc Geol Assoc*, 72 (1961) 221–38

——. 'Dorset Geology 1950–60,' *PDNH&AS* 84 (1962) 77–91

——. '*Dorset Coast Poole to Chesil Beach*,' Geologists' Assoc Guide No 22 (1969)

Howarth, M. K. 'The Middle Lias of the Dorset Coast,' *Quart Jour Geol Soc*, 113 (1957) 185–204

Jackson, J. F. 'The Junction Bed of the Middle & Upper Lias on the Dorset Coast,' *Quart Jour Geol Soc* 82 (1926) 490–525

Lang, W. D. 'Geology of the Charmouth Cliffs Beach & Foreshore,' *Proc Geol Assoc*, 25 (1914) 293–360

———. 'The Blue Lias of the Devon & Dorset Coasts,' *Proc Geol Assoc*, 35 (1924) 169–85

———. 'The Lower Lias of Charmouth & The Vale of Marshwood,' *Proc Geol Assoc*, 43 (1932) 97–126

Laughton, A. S. 'The S Labrador Sea & The Evolution of the N Atlantic,' *Nature* 232, 612

Lees, G. M. & Cox, P. T. 'The Geological Basis of the Search for Oil in Great Britain by the D'Arcy Exploration Co', *Quart Jour Geol Soc*, 93 (1937) 156–94

May, V. J. 'Reclamation & Shoreline Change in Poole Harbour, Dorset,' *PDNH&AS* 90 (1968) 141–54

McFadyen, W. A. *Geological Highlights of the West Country* (Butterworth, 1970)

Mottram, B. H. 'Notes on the Structure of the Poxwell Pericline, and the Ridgeway Fault at Bincombe Tunnel, Dorset,' *PDNH&AS* 71 (1949) 175–83

Mottram, B. H. & House, M. R. 'The Structure of the N Margin of the Poxwell Pericline,' *PDNH&AS*, 76 (1956) 129–35

Pepin, C. E. *Hengistbury Head* (Bournemouth Ed Ctte, 1967)

Phillips, W. J. 'The Structures in the Jurassic & Cretaceous Rocks on the Dorset Coast between White Nothe & Mupe Bay,' *Proc Geol Assoc*, 75 (1964) 373–406

Richardson, L. 'The Inferior Oolite & Contiguous Deposits of the Burton Bradstock-Broadwindsor District of Dorset,' *Proc Cotteswold Nat Field Club*, 23 (1928–30) 35–68, 149–85, 253–64

Robinson, A. H. W. 'The Harbour Entrances of Poole, Christchurch & Pagham,' *Geogr Jour*, 121 (1955) 33–50

Rowe, A. W. 'The Zones of the White Chalk of the English Coast, Part II, ' *Proc Geol Assoc*, 17 (1901) 1–76

Simpson, Scott. 'On the Trace Fossil Chondrites,' *Quart Jour Geol Soc*, 112 (1957) 475–95

SW Stone Co. *Portland Stone* (London, 1933)

Sylvester Bradley, P. C. 'Field Meeting at Weymouth, Dorset,' *Proc Geol Assoc*, 59 (1948) 141–7

Walkden, G. & Oppe, E. 'In the Footsteps of Dinosaurs,' *Amateur Geologist*, 3 pt 2 (1969)

West, I. M. 'On the Occurrence of Celestine in the Caps & Broken Beds of Durlston Head, Dorset,' *Proc Geol Assoc*, 71 (1960) 391–401

West, I. M., Shearman, D. J. & Pugh, M. E. 'Whitsun Field Meeting, Weymouth Area,' *Proc Geol Assoc*, 80 (1969) 331–40

White, H. J. O. *Geology of Bournemouth*, Mem Geol Surv (HMSO, 1917)

——. *Geology of the Country S & W of Shaftesbury*, Mem Geol Surv (HMSO, 1923)

Williams, C. & McKenzie, D. 'The Evolution of the NE Atlantic,' *Nature* 232, 168–73

Wilson, V. et al. *Geology of the Country Around Bridport & Yeovil*, Mem Geol Surv (HMSO, 1958)

Young, D. 'Brickmaking in Dorset,' *PDNH&AS*, 93 (1972) 213–42

PDNH&AS is a source of much information and useful articles, especially the annual Geology reports. All the publications listed contain further important bibliographical references, supplementing the short list which space permits here.

Appendix—Table of Rock Strata

Era and period	Stage	Zone	Strata	Notable horizons and fold movements
Quaternary HOLOCENE			Blown sand, sand and shingle beaches, alluvium and peat, tufa	Blashenwell tufa
PLEISTOCENE 2 million years ago		Head, coombe rock, raised beach of Portland, plateau and angular flint gravels		Second major folding, the Alpine, 25 million years ago
	UNCONFORMITY			
Tertiary OLIGOCENE	Lattorfian		Creechbarrow Limestone	
EOCENE	Cusian / Ypresian		Bagshot beds, London Clay, Reading Beds	Agglestone Grit
PALAEOCENE 65 million years ago	Landenian			
	UNCONFORMITY			
Mesozoic →	Senonian	Belemnitella mucronata	Upper Chalk	
		Actinocamax quadratus		
		Offaster pilula		
		Marsupites testudinarius		
		Micraster coranguinum		
		Micraster cortestudinarium		
		Holaster planus		
	Turonian	Terebratulina lata	Middle Chalk	

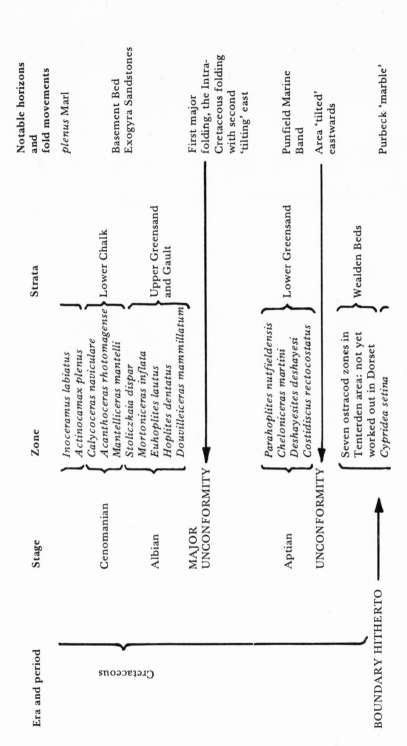

Era and period	Stage	Zone	Strata	Notable horizons and fold movements
Cretaceous	Cenomanian	Inoceramus labiatus / Actinocamax plenus / Calycoceras naviculare / Acanthoceras rhotomagense / Mantelliceras mantelli	Lower Chalk	plenus Marl
				Basement Bed Exogyra Sandstones
	Albian	Stoliczkaia dispar / Mortoniceras inflata / Euhoplites lautus / Hoplites dentatus / Douvilleiceras mammillatum	Upper Greensand and Gault	
	MAJOR UNCONFORMITY			First major folding, the Intra-Cretaceous folding with second 'tilting' east
	Aptian	Parahoplites nutfieldensis / Cheloniceras martini / Deshayesites deshayesi / Costidiscus rectocostatus	Lower Greensand	Punfield Marine Band
				Area 'tilted' eastwards
	UNCONFORMITY	Seven ostracod zones in Tenterden area: not yet worked out in Dorset / Cypridea setina	Wealden Beds	Purbeck 'marble'

BOUNDARY HITHERTO

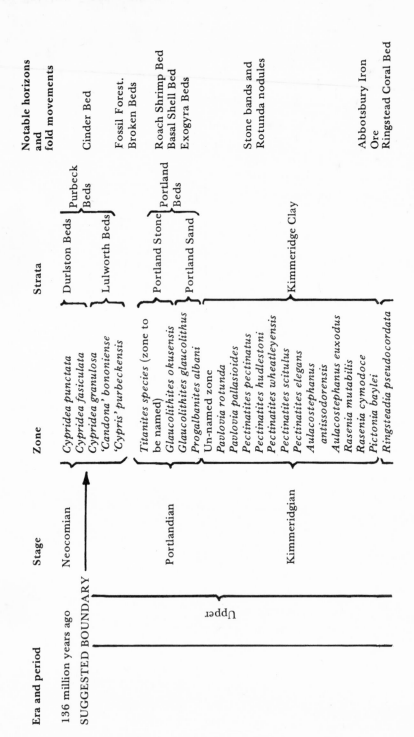

Era and period	Stage	Zone	Strata	Notable horizons and fold movements
136 million years ago SUGGESTED BOUNDARY Upper	Neocomian	*Cypridea punctata* *Cypridea fasiculata* *Cypridea granulosa* *'Candona' bononiense* *'Cypris' purbeckensis*	Durlston Beds — Purbeck Beds Lulworth Beds — Purbeck Beds	Cinder Bed Fossil Forest. Broken Beds
	Portlandian	*Titanites* species (zone to be named) *Glaucolithites okusensis* *Glaucolithites glaucolithus* *Progalbanites albani* Un-named zone *Pavlovia rotunda* *Pavlovia pallasioides*	Portland Stone — Portland Beds Portland Sand	Roach Shrimp Bed Basal Shell Bed Exogyra Beds
	Kimmeridgian	*Pectinatites pectinatus* *Pectinatites hudlestoni* *Pectinatites wheatleyensis* *Pectinatites scitulus* *Pectinatites elegans* *Aulacostephanus antissodorensis* *Aulacostephanus euxodus* *Rasenia mutabilis* *Rasenia cymodoce* *Pictonia baylei* *Ringsteadia pseudocordata*	Kimmeridge Clay	Stone bands and Rotunda nodules Abbotsbury Iron Ore Ringstead Coral Bed

Era and period		Stage	Zone	Strata		Notable horizons and fold movements
Jurassic	Middle	Oxfordian	*Decipia decipiens*	Corallian Beds		
			Perisphinctes cautisnigrae			
			Gregoryceras transversarium			Pisolite
			Perisphinctes plicatilis			Red Nodule Beds
			Cardioceras cordatum			
			Quenstedtoceras mariae	Oxford Clay & Kellaways Beds		
		Callovian	*Quenstedtoceras lamberti*			
			Peltoceras athleta			
			Erymnoceras coronatum			
			Kosmoceras jason			
			Sigalloceras calloviense			
			Proplanulites koenigi			
			Macrocephalites macrocephalus	Cornbrash		
		Bathonian	*Clydoniceras discus*	Forest Marble	Great Oolite Series	Boueti Bed
			Oppelia aspidoides			
			Prohecticoceras retrocostatum	Fullers Earth		
			Morrisceras morrisi			Elongata Bed
			Tulites subcontractus			Wattonensis Beds
			Procerites gracilis			
			Zigzagiceras zigzag			Zigzag Bed
			Parkinsonia parkinsoni			
			Garantiana garantiana	Inferior Oolite with several non-sequences		'Obliqua' Bed OLD BASEMENT FOLDS ACTIVE
			Stenoceras subfurcatum			
			Stephanoceras humphriesanum			Snuff Boxes

Era and period	Stage	Zone	Strata	Notable horizons and fold movements
	Bajocian	*Sonninia Sowerbyi* *Graphoceras concavum* *Ludwigia murchisonae* *Tmetoceras scissum* *Leioceras opalinum*	Bridport Sands Downcliff Clay	
	Taorcian	*Dumortiera levesquei* *Grammoceras thouarsense* *Haugia variabilis* *Hildoceras bifrons* *Harpoceras falcifer* *Dactylioceras tenuicostatum*	Junction Bed with several non-sequences	MOVEMENTS IN BASEMENT
Lower or Lias	Pleinsbachian	*Pleuroceras spinatum* *Amaltheus margaritatus* *Prodactylioceras davoei* *Tragophylloceras ibex* *Uptonia jamesoni*	Eype Clay etc Green Ammonite Beds Belemnite Marls	Margaritatus Bed; Starfish & Nodule Beds; Three Tiers Red Band Belemnite Stone
	Sinemurian	*Echioceras raricostatum* *Oxynoticeras oxynotum* *Asteroceras obtusum* *Caenisites turneri* *Arnioceras semicostatum* *Arietites bucklandi*	Black Ven Marls Shales with Beef	*stellare* nodules *birchi* nodules
	Hettangian	*Schlotheimia angulata* *Alsatites liasicus* *Psiloceras planorbis*	Blue Lias	

Table based on Cope, House, Sylvester-Bradley, et al

Acknowledgements

I am greatly indebted to Dr E. B. Selwood of Exeter University for reading and commenting on the script; to Mr Bryan Jones of English China Clays for permission to visit the company's ball clay workings and advice on the sections concerning the industry; to Mr J. Sykes and staff of Watts Blake Bearne & Co; to Dr John Cope of Swansea; to Mr S. W. Paine of California Farm Quarry, Swanage; to Messrs. Suttle of Swanage Quarries; to Mr S. B. Hounsell of Easton Masonry Works, Portland; and especially to Mrs M. T. Davies for typing the book for me. Many other people have kindly answered my queries, given permission for access, etc. Any geological study inevitably draws on the published maps and memoirs of the Institute of Geological Sciences and grateful acknowledgement is made to the Director for permission to use them.

The quotation from *The Return of the Native* by Thomas Hardy is by permission of the Trustees of the Hardy Estate and Macmillan, London and Basingstoke.

JOHN W. PERKINS

Index